A Short Course in Industrial Design

A Short Course in Industrial Design

Eskild Tjalve

Senior Lecturer, Department of Engineering
Design, The Technical University of Denmark

NEWNES - BUTTERWORTHS
LONDON - BOSTON
Sydney - Wellington - Durban - Toronto

THE BUTTERWORTH GROUP

UNITED KINGDOM	Butterworth & Co (Publishers) Ltd London: 88 Kingsway, WC2B 6AB
AUSTRALIA	Butterworths Pty Ltd Sydney: 586 Pacific Highway, Chatswood, NSW 2067 Also at Melbourne, Brisbane, Adelaide and Perth
CANADA	Butterworth & Co (Canada) Ltd Scarborough: 2265 Midland Avenue, Scarborough, Ontario, MIP 4S1
NEW ZEALAND	Butterworths of New Zealand Ltd Wellington: T & W Young Building, 77—85 Customhouse Quay 1, CPO Box 472
SOUTH AFRICA	Butterworth & Co (South Africa) (Pty) Ltd Durban: 152—154 Gale Street
USA	Butterworths (Publishers) Inc Boston: 10 Tower Office Park, Woburn, Mass. 01801

First published in Denmark in 1976 as 'Systematisk udformning af
industriprodukter'

First published in English 1979

British Library Cataloguing in Publication Data

Tjalve, Eskild
  A short course in industrial design.
  1. Engineering design
  I. Title
  620'.0042   TA174   78-41280

  ISBN 0-408-00388-X

Typeset by Butterworths Litho Preparation Department

Printed in Scotland by Thomson Litho Ltd., East Kilbride

Preface

The creation of a new product takes in many levels of activity and many skills, of which the first and foremost are those of design engineers and industrial designers. It is easy to recognise the extremes when comparing the responsibilities of the design engineer and the industrial designer, but not so easy to say where the responsibility of one ends and the other begins.

The design engineer is involved in design which is often known by other names, e.g. sketching, detail design, dimensioning, etc. A considerable part of the work of design engineers and industrial designers consists of the same activities, i.e. formulation of suggestions of shape, 'modelling' of these (sketching, drawing or hardware modelling), investigating and appraising the various possibilities. These activities involve the creative mind at many levels and are the subject of this book, which not only introduces the student to the principles of evolving a design, but surveys the criteria by which these are assessed. Throughout this book the word 'designer' has been used as a blanket term for people working with design (i.e. engineers, designers and others) of products.

The contents of this book should be seen as part of the design technique. In the overall plan for project evaluation and design only the methods connected with the final phases of design project have been described.

The danger of formulating systematic methods in connection with construction work, is that others are led into thinking that a systematic approach necessarily gives the right answer. This is just not so. The most effective solution is achieved by the right balance of systematics and intuition. The systematic approach should therefore be seen as the foundation for the appropriate attitude to innovation, namely an understanding of the fact that one can, through a conscious effort look objectively and systematically at all the design criteria and premises on which any particular solution is based.

Existing products have to a great extent been used as examples. These are included particularly where they illustrate different approaches to the same problem and different results — and not because they are particularly good or bad. There is thus no implied evaluation in their presentation.

I would like to thank those companies which have contributed to the examples by submitting material of various kinds. The photographs which are not acknowledged were taken on my behalf by Frank Schmidt, to whom I am very grateful.

It is my hope that many of those who are involved in the evolution of products will find this book useful whether they are engineers or designers. I also hope that the book will fill a gap in the literature connected with the teaching of engineering design in the schools of engineering. In the traditional approach, a material object requires a rough drawing before one can get down to the necessary specific calculations and detailing. A lot of time is rightly used on these essential procedures, yet so often no one will question how the idea behind any particular scheme has emerged. It is too common a mistake to regard the first idea for a design as the only one or even as the best. Lastly I hope that the book may be an inspiration to industrial designers in training and in practice, as it must be important for designers to get an idea of the phases a complex product goes through, as well as a general view of the relevant criteria for evaluation.

Eskild Tjalve

Contents

1 CREATION OF A PRODUCT

1. Creation of a Product

1.1 The idea of form

A very great part of our world consists of objects which have one fundamental property, form: i.e. a shape, a certain arrangement of parts and an overall structure. Form may arise as follows (Figure 1):

1. An uncontrolled process, where the form depends solely on the conditions of the environment, e.g. pebbles, mountain ranges.
2. A process controlled by physical and chemical laws as well as the conditions of the environment, e.g. ice crystals, mica.
3. A process controlled by genes and the conditions of the environment, e.g. living organisms.
4. A process controlled by the wishes of men or animals and the conditions of the environment, e.g. manufactured products, a beaver's dam, birds' nests.

Now that manufactured products increasingly dominate our everyday world — indeed where whole environments are man-made — we need to analyse more closely the processes by which form is determined, so that we may design our environment as much to our liking as possible.

As a first attempt at this analysis let us examine the valve in Figure 2. The design of the valve and the parts from which it is assembled is as follows:

The two connecting pieces are hexagonal because one must be able to assemble the valve with an adjustable spanner.

The rotating nut under the handweel is also hexagonal so that it can be tightened with a spanner. The handwheel is round because the hand must be able to grasp it firmly in all positions.

The spindle is threaded because of its function, which is to transform the rotary movement (of the handwheel) into one of translation (of the valve seat).

The valve seat is annular because one must be able to face it off with a milling cutter to make it fit tightly against the gasket.

The inner cavity of the valve is shaped to facilitate flow.

The outer form of the valve consists of two intersecting cylinders.

The cylinder form is determined by the mould from which the valve housing is cast.

Similar comments to the above can be made on the cup and saucer shown in Figure 3:

The cup and saucer have rotational symmetry, either because they are thrown on the potter's wheel or, (if they were made in a mould) simply because cups and saucers traditionally have rotational symmetry.

The cup is cylindrical because a certain appearance was desired.

The cup is smaller in diameter at the base partly because it is then stackable and partly for reasons of appearance.

The notch in the base of the cup lets the water drain away if it is washed (upside down) in a washing up machine.

The shape of the handle ensures that the part which is held does not get too hot when the cup is being used.

The edge of the saucer is turned up because it must be able to hold liquid spilt from the cup.

Even if these two examples are a little simplified they still show clearly that the design of a product and its elements depends on many different factors,

3

4

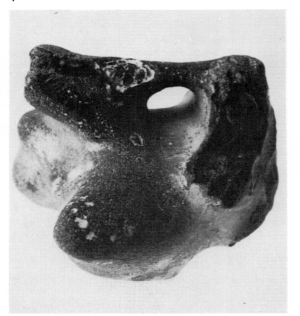

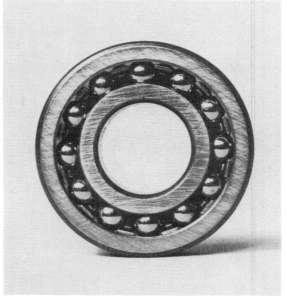

Figure 1   Form can arise in four ways

Figure 2   The form of the valve is determined by a large number of factors

e.g. manufacturing process, function, ease of handling, appearance and economics. Another very important factor, which we must not forget, is the person who designs the product. However many requirements there are in the specification of the design, there will always be room for the designer to express his ideas and personal judgement.

An understanding of the factors which influence the design must be built on a knowledge of the various stages in the life of the product. In the following pages, therefore, we will examine a model of the life of a product from inception to destruction, as well as a more detailed model of the way in which a product comes into being.

Figure 3   Many factors determine the form of a cup (Rørstrand)

1.2 Life of the product

All products are created, used and eventually discarded. Let us, therefore, examine a little more closely what happens to a product before, during and after use.

When a product is used it performs a process which brings about an external change from one state to another. It is the need for this transformation that has caused the product to be created, for example:

Scissors: A whole sheet of paper — paper divided into two pieces.
File: A blank with burrs — a blank with chamfered edges.
Television: A person with a need for entertainment and information — a person entertained and informed.
Extruder: Plastic granules — continuous length of plastic profile with the required cross section.

Before the product is used the user has brought it from a dealer, who in turn has brought it from the manufacturer. When it has either served its purpose, worn out or broken, it is destroyed.

If these events are arranged in sequence, we can illustrate the life of the product as shown in Figure 4. The starting point is the use for which the product is intended. The first phase is the design process in which possible methods of satisfying the user needs are examined, and in which the finally chosen product is completely specified. For products which are to be produced in great numbers, the design and choice of production method follow next, but for the sake of clarity this phase has been left out in Figure 4. Next comes the product manufacturing process, after which the product is sold to the dealer, from whom it is resold to the consumer. Only now can the product function according to its intended purpose. The life of the product ends with destruction. This process can be active, where the product may be crushed, taken apart of melted down, or passive, where it rusts, crumbles or decomposes, etc.

Figure 4 shows that, ideally, information is fed into the design process from all other product-related activities. Effective design is only possible if the designer is aware of what happens beyond the drawing board and in other departments. Thus, the product is specified during the design process, but with requirements and wishes from all the other stages in mind.

It is important to realise that Figure 4 shows the general course of an industrially manufactured product. In products that are designed and made by the same person the first two processes can be combined. Note also that there may be other input to the design process other than information on need or function, such as an idea for a product or new competing products. The input shown in Figure 4, however, is considered the general one, because in the other situations one still has to go back and start with the need.

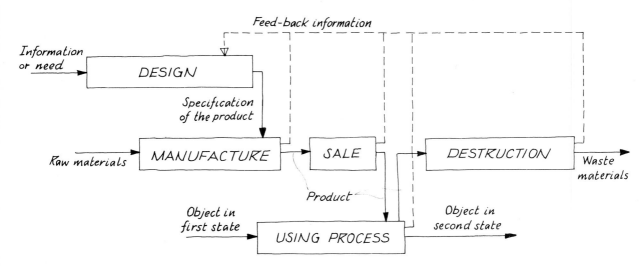

Figure 4   *Showing the processes in the life of a product*

1.3 Properties of the product

Any object (product, machine, or system) possesses characteristic properties. Some of these properties may be desired, but others may be more or less unwanted. The most important property of all is the primary function of the product, because it is this that helps the user in his need. The other desirable properties may be: pleasing appearance, ease of handling, safety, durability and reliability.

Before the product is designed the required properties should be listed by the designer, perhaps in collaboration with the user. During the design period when the product is created, it is these properties that determine the decisions and choices that are made.

Unfortunately one cannot design a product in such a way that the desired properties are determined one after the other, for they are not independent variables. We find, however, that five properties can be distinguished from all others, in that together they completely define the product. They are:

For the product as a whole:	Structure (i.e. the elements of the product and their relationship)
For each element:	Form Material Dimension Surface

These five properties are the *basic properties*. It is important to emphasise that these are the variables which the designer can manipulate, and it is by successively deciding on these that a product is created. Thus all the other properties, desirable as well as undesirable, are derived from the basic properties.

The aim in designing is that the qualities present in the finished product should correspond to the properties required. As this aim, however, is not always achieved, we must distinguish between the desired properties and the realised ones.

Thus we can arrive at a model of the design process as shown in Figure 5. This shows the step-by-step process from the analysis of the problem to the finished product.

In the initial analysis stage, the problem is examined from all sides. This results on the one hand in a concrete formulation of the desired function, and on the other hand, in a list of the desired properties which constitute the criteria that must make up the background for the selection of solutions.

Next follows the stage of synthesis, i.e. the stage in which the product is created. This is done by roughly determining step by step on the basic properties of structure, form, material, dimension, and surface.

When the basic properties are decided on, the design of the product is finished, and it can be manufactured. After manufacture the product exists, and possesses some *'realised properties.'*, which hopefully are close to the 'desired properties' that were formulated during the initial analysis.

1.4 The step-by-step creation of the product

The design model shown in Figure 5 is a greatly simplified one, that serves only to give a general view of the design process. It cannot be used as a recipe for designing a product. It can, however, be elaborated to try to achieve this. As we are primarily concerned with the quality of 'form', we will only make the model more detailed in the stages where the basic properties are laid down.

We can call the detailed model the *product synthesis,* as it shows the individual steps through which

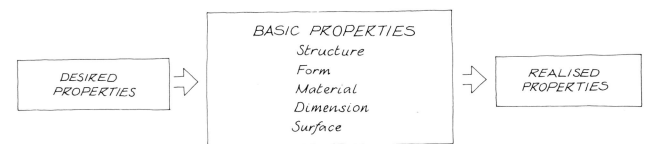

Figure 5   The basic properties are the variables which the designer can manipulate. The other properties of the product depend on these

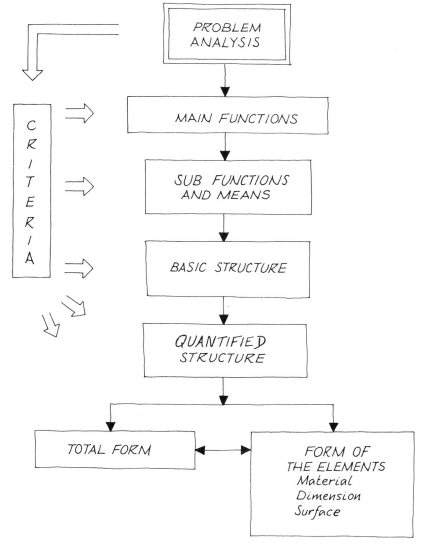

Figure 6   The product synthesis. A model of the design process showing the stages
in the creation of a product

the product is created, see Figure 6. The black arrows show the time sequence. The product synthesis takes as its starting point the two outputs from the problem analysis, namely on the one hand the formulation of the desired function — the main function (possibly several sub-ordinate main functions) — on the other hand the list of desired properties, which can also be described as criteria for an optimum product.

In Figure 5 we saw that the next step is the determination of the structure. In the product synthesis this very important stage is divided into a series of steps, beginning with a division of the desired function into sub-functions. Then follows an examination of possible means of realising the sub-functions, a combination of these into a basic structure and finally an adaptation into a quantified structure, where critical parameters are optimised and where the relative arrangement of the elements is determined.

Form is treated in two parallel branches, since the total form and the form of the constituent elements are determined simultaneously. The detailed form of the elements includes a specification of materials, dimensions and surfaces.

We see from the product synthesis, Figure 6, that the criteria for an optimum product are used through the whole design process as a guideline and control for each step where a decision is taken.

The following paragraphs outline the individual stages in the product synthesis and typical examples are given.

Main functions

The *main function* of a product is the way in which output is determined by input. If we conceive the product as a compound system we can discuss functions at all levels from the function of the total system (main function, or possibly several parallel main functions) to the functions of sub-systems and of elements (sub-functions).

The idea of function is a very important tool for analysing a problem into a series of clearly formulated components that express what the product must be able to do.

Sub-functions and means

By *means.* we understand a solution, i.e. a method, a sub-system or an element, with which a given function can be realised. The division of the main function into sub-functions and further into sub-sub-functions, etc takes place alternately with the search for means to realise these. One possible procedure consists of arranging a so-called function/means tree.

Figure 7 shows how the first stages in the function/means tree for an automatic teamaker may look. Theoretically the function/means tree can be detailed until the means become machine elements, or parts of machine elements. We stop when we have found means to the most important sub-functions.

Basic structure

A solution is achieved by connecting one process for each sub-function, which we call the basic structure. The basic structure can be expressed in block diagrams, working (or basic) drawings (machine symbols, hydraulic, pneumatic, electric symbols, etc) or otherwise simplified drawings. No decisions are made at this stage as to 'quantities' such as dimensions, relative arrangement etc. Figure 18 shows different basic structures of the teamaker (see Figure 7).

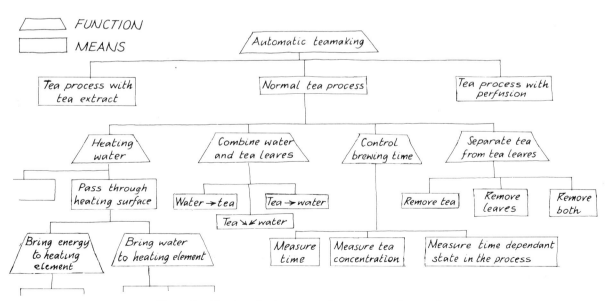

Figure 7   The function/means tree for an automatic teamaker

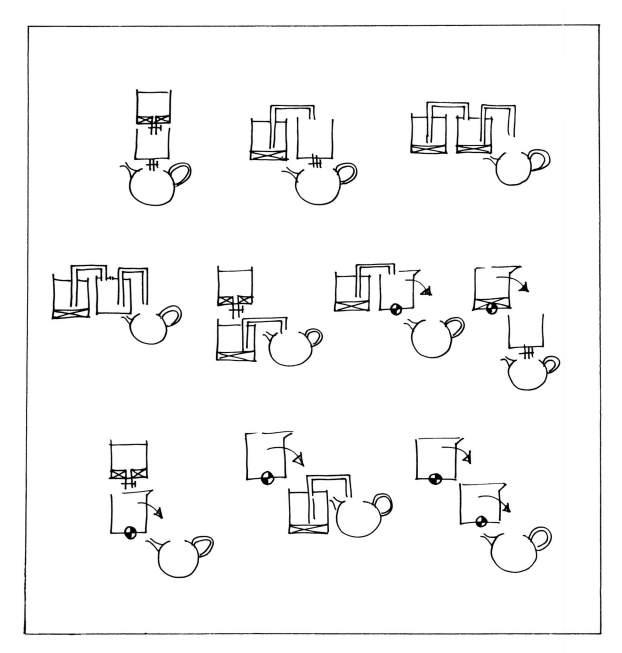

Figure 8   Alternative basic structures for an automatic teamaker

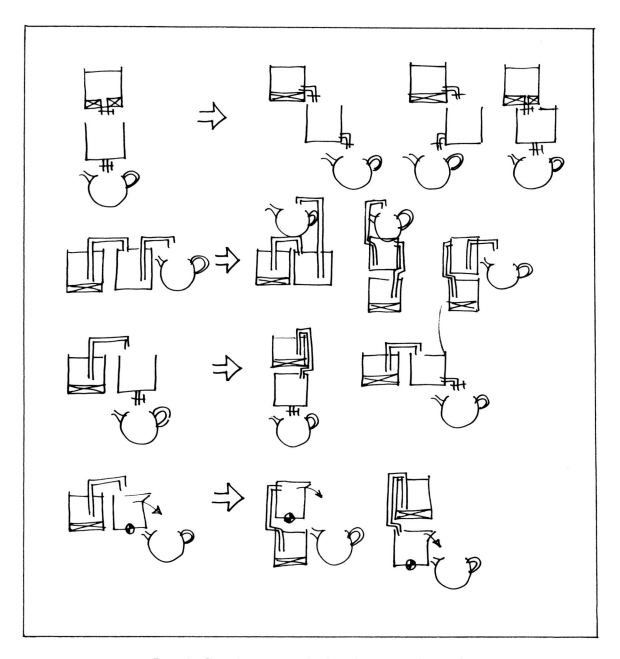

Figure 9   Quantified structures for the main elements of a teamaker

Quantified structure

The quantified structure is one where the important parameters of the individual elements are optimised and specified, together with the relative arrangement of the elements. However, nothing is yet decided concerning the form design of the elements. Different quantified structures are shown in Figure 9.

Total form

The total form of the product is determined alternately with the form of the elements. The requirements of the total design depend on the product we are dealing with. If aesthetic criteria are important (i.e. in cars, boats, cameras, etc) the design of the elements must be adapted to the total design.

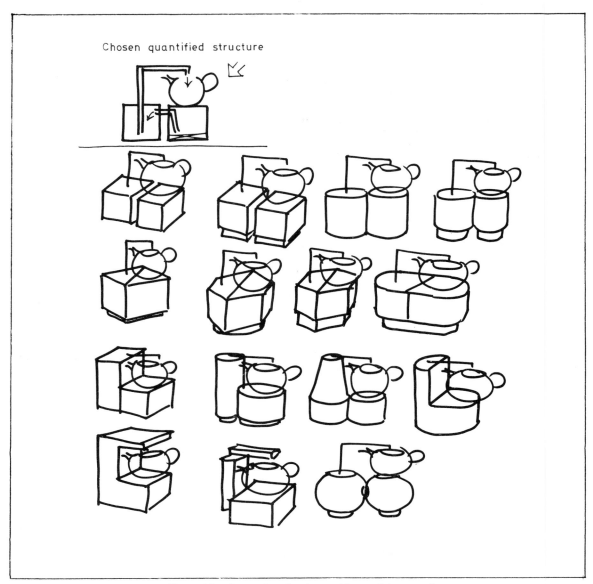

Chosen quantified structure

Figure 10   *Suggestions for the total form of the teamaker*

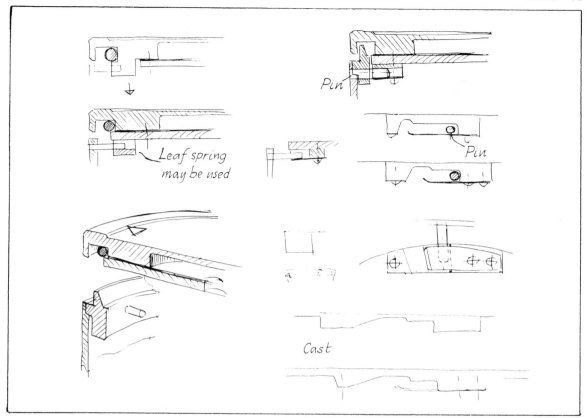

Figure 11   Sketches made in connection with the detail design elements of the teamaker

If technical and economic criteria are what matters most (i.e. carburettors, gearboxes, satellites, etc) the design of the elements must take precedence over the total design.

Form of the elements

The form design of the individual elements is made at the detail design stage of the product. The various considerations of the form of the functional areas make a good starting point for this stage. The criteria which matter at this stage are primarily determined by function, strength and manufacturing methods.

Typical activities at this stage are, first of all, calculation, sketching and drawing. Free-hand sketches done in a quick and light technique are extremely useful, see Figure 11. Gradually, as the form of the elements is settled, the sketches are replaced by layouts, prepared with a drawing machine, and scale drawings.

The final design of each element requires decisions on material, dimension, surface, tolerance and production technology.

The elements of the product are specified in working drawings which express four of the fundamental properties, form, material, dimension and surface, as well as further information such as quantities to be produced, possible manufacturing process, number of the drawing, date, etc. The fifth fundamental property, the structure, is specified in assembly drawings which show how the component elements are to be assembled, see Figure 12. The finished teamaker is shown in Figure 13.

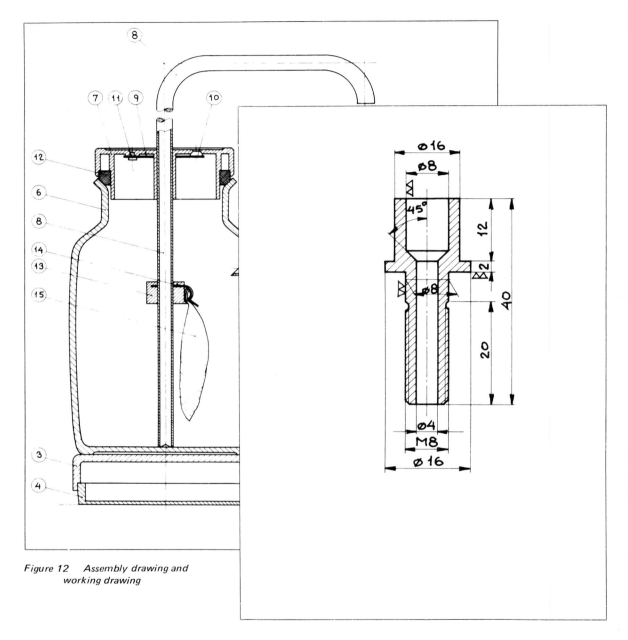

*Figure 12   Assembly drawing and
working drawing*

Product synthesis

Each phase in the product synthesis brings the designer nearer his goal — the finished product. In spite of the changing contents of the phases they all show a typical course:

1. The search for solutions,
2. Examination of the solutions,
3. Evaluation and choice of solutions for further work.

Figure 13   The finished teamaker (The Laboratory for Engineering design, The Technical University of Denmark)

This course is illustrated in Figure 14, where the number of solutions is shown as a function of time. Each peak corresponds to a phase in the product synthesis.

The search for solutions is carried out by generating ideas either intuitively or systematically, the most appropriate methods depending on the phase. The aim in seeking many solutions in a given phase is to explore the 'space' created by the great number of theoretically possible solutions. It is seldom possible to examine all solutions, as they are usually innumerable. But the 'solution space' should still be examined thoroughly so that all the main types of solution are included. Only then we can say with reasonable certainty that we can choose the best solution.

The evaluation of the solutions is made on the basis of criteria which vary with the phase and the degree of detail in the solutions. An intuitive evaluation may thus be sufficient in the early phases, while later on it may be necessary to apply quite a number of mutually weighted criteria.

The final result — the product — thus depends on two fundamentally different factors, firstly on the ideas that are born, and secondly on the criteria that decide which ideas are chosen. A closer analysis of the idea of form can be made from these two points of view. Thus the next chapter deals with the methods that can be applied in searching for form ideas, while Chapter 3 'Form Factors' is about the factors that make up the background for the selection criteria.

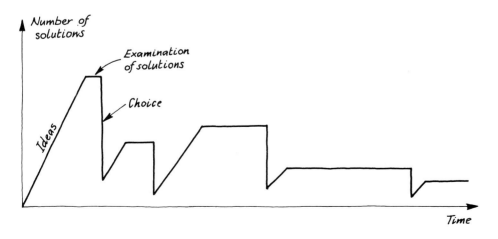

Figure 14   The search for and examination of solutions, evaluation and choice are a characteristic sequence in the product synthesis

2 METHODS USED IN FORM DESIGN

2. Methods Used in Form Design

2.1 Limitations

The final decisions on a product's form normally take place in the last phases of the design process, but it is important to realise that before this, the designer has already been reflecting and making decisions that have a fundamental influence on the form. In the previous chapter (section 1.4) we saw an example of this. Let us, however, consider a number of examples which more directly illustrate the importance of the early decisions on the form of the product.

The main function of the product — established during the first phase of product synthesis — has a crucial influence on the type of product, e.g. whether it is a machine or a tool. Two products with different main functions will therefore be so different that it is impossible to create one 'in between' — they are simply fundamentally different. Figure 15 shows an example of this, namely a calculator and an abacus.

The calculator fulfills the same need for an European as the abacus for a Chinese.

The way in which the main function is broken down into sub-functions, as well as the means chosen, to satisfy the sub-functions is just as important for the design as the main function. This can be illustrated by a comparison of two products with the same main function but with a different basic structure.

Figure 16 shows two different jacks, both with the main function — to transform a rotational manual movement into a very powerful vertical one. The form of the two jacks differs fundamentally, because different means have been used to realize the individual sub functions, i.e. the basic structure is different. We can also note that the form of one cannot be gradually changed into the form of the other.

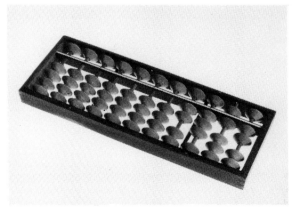

Figure 15   Desk calculator and Japanese abacus or counting frame. The two products fulfil the same need, but the main function is different (Desk calculator reproduced by courtesy of Canon)

19

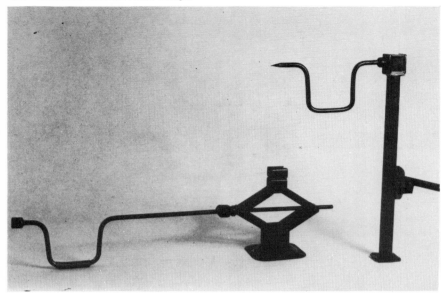

Figure 16   Two car jacks having the same main function (i.e. similar input and output) but different basic structures

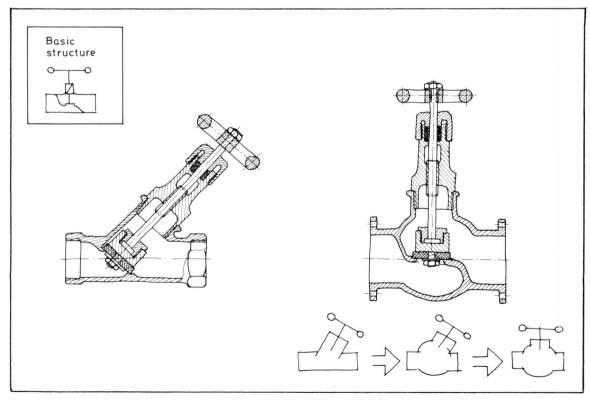

Figure 17   Two valves with the same basic structure but with different quantified structures. The lower illustration shows how one structure can be gradually changed into the other

The quantified structure brings us to a level in product synthesis where we can move gradually from one solution to another. In Figure 17 the two valves have different quantified structures but the same basic structure, i.e. from the point of view of function they contain the same elements. They are distinguished by the different form design of the elements and by the different angle of the spindle and the handwheel. The way in which the form design of the two valves can be modified, so that we can move gradually from one to the other, is also illustrated.

Form synthesis methods aim to cover the whole range of design solutions. We have seen that for a chosen basic structure the form design can be changed smoothly from one solution to another. The methods for form synthesis can therefore be naturally described as variation methods where some charac-teristic parameters are varied in such a way that the whole solution space is covered. The question of which parameters can be profitably varied will be examined in the following chapters, where the methods are related to the last phases in product synthesis, namely the quantified structure, the total form and the form of the elements.

2.2 Structure variation

The structure variation method

Consider the three coffee makers shown in Figure 18. They all work on the same principle (i.e. with a similar basic structure). But why are two of them alike, while the third one is quite different? The answer lies in the quantified structure.

Figure 18 Three different coffee makers with the same basic structure. The shape of the top two products is almost identical. Why is the one below different? (Courtesty of Melitta, NG Electric, Braun)

In the first two the relative arrangement of the component elements is similar, while in the last one it is different. The relative arrangement of the component elements is an important feature of a quantified structure. Another important feature is the dimensions of the parts, in this case the sizes of the containers and the distance between these.

The relative arrangement and the dimensions of the component elements can be used as variation parameters in the search for design solutions. This method can be called 'the structure variation method.' The greatest effect is achieved if the individual solutions are illustrated (possibly modelled in three dimensions) in a technique where all superfluous details are left out. In this way one saves time in the formulation of the solutions as well as clarity when comparing them.

Figure 19 shows the basic structure for coffee makers, together with how a number of quantified structures created by variation of the relative arrangement and of the dimensions of the elements.

Figure 20 shows examples of typical coffee makers. It demonstrates how a common quantified

structure for any two products gives a common design character, while different quantified structures produce wide differences in the design.

The structure variation method is an easy method of generating ideas for alternative structures. The method is based on the view that a number of suggested solutions are needed before a solution can definitely be characterised as good. The method has been tried in different project situations, and it can be applied at many levels, e.g. in both the building up of the total system and in the creation of small sub-systems.

Quantified structure can be used from two points of view, which differ in whether the functional connection between the elements is included or not. If these functional connections are ignored, the structure variation method gives a number of suggestions for a very rough construction of the product. If the functional connections are included, we get a definite further development of the basic structure, with the aim of optimising and specifying the parameters involved. This is shown by the examples given in the following paragraphs.

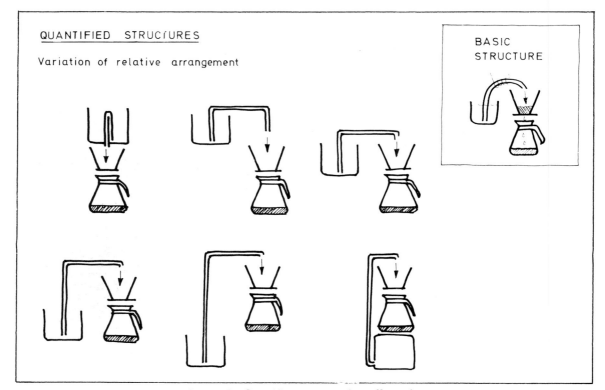

Figure 19   Quantified structures for coffee makers

Figure 20   Various types of coffee makers. See also quantified structures in Figure 19 (Courtesy of Siemens, Krups, Melitta, Philips, and Braun)

Structure variation of the main elements

The elements that most influence a product's form design are, of course, the main ones. We may therefore conveniently apply the structure variation method to a few of the main elements of the product, in order that a first survey of the possibilities for the design may be carried out. The sketches or models made at this stage give a background for a first rough sorting of the solutions according to such criteria as space, operation and appearance.

Figure 21 shows a number of quantified structures for a vacuum cleaner, together with the relative arrangement of the three main elements. The functional connection between the elements is not indicated. Figure 22 shows some modern vacuum cleaners, where we can see how greatly the relative arrangement of the elements influences the design.

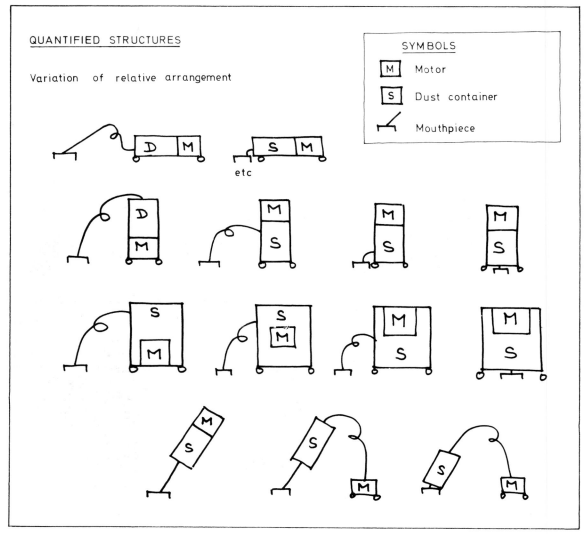

Figure 21   Quantified structures for vacuum cleaners

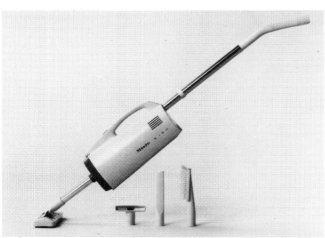

Figure 22   Vacuum cleaners with different quantified structures. (See also Figure 21). (Courtesy of Nilfisk and Miele)

Let us now see how the structure variation method can be applied to a microscope. The basic structure of the microscope is characterised by the lenses and image planes involved. To determine the derived structure, one needs information on the size and focal length of the lenses, the distance between them and their relative arrangement. Figure 23 shows quantified structures based on variation of the relative arrangement of the tube and the object plane in relation to the table.

The functional connections between the elements (e.g. the direction of the rays and focussing) are not included in the quantified structures, but they can be drawn very quickly. The two microscopes in Figure 24 are constructed with different quantified structures, which can be clearly seen from their very different designs.

Often it is possible to use yet another variation parameter, namely the number of each of the constituent types of element. In principle a variation of the number belongs to the basic structure, but in cases where an element can be divided into several or doubled — without altering the character of the basic structure — the number may with equal right be varied under the quantified structure.

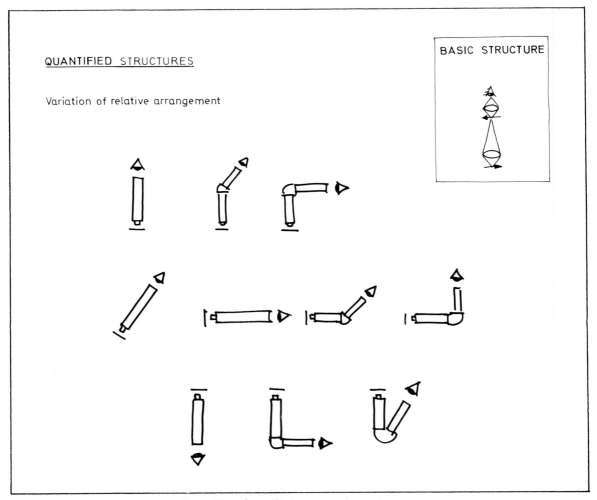

Figure 23   Quantified structures for a microscope

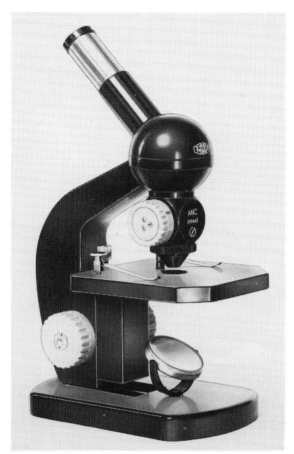

Figure 24   Microscope with different quantified structures.
(Courtesy of Olympus and Monolynx)

Figure 25 shows possible quantified structures for road rollers, where the variation parameters are the relative arrangement and the number of the elements. The elements we examine are: wheels, engine and position of the operator. Only road rollers built on the traditional principle, where rolling wheels and transport wheels are identical are considered.

In Figure 25, note that the range of solutions is narrowed considerably due to the fact that all the wheels must be on the same level, and that no element may lie below this level.

In Figure 25, note also that the key to the systematic arrangement covering the whole spectrum of solutions   lies in the small framed figures. These

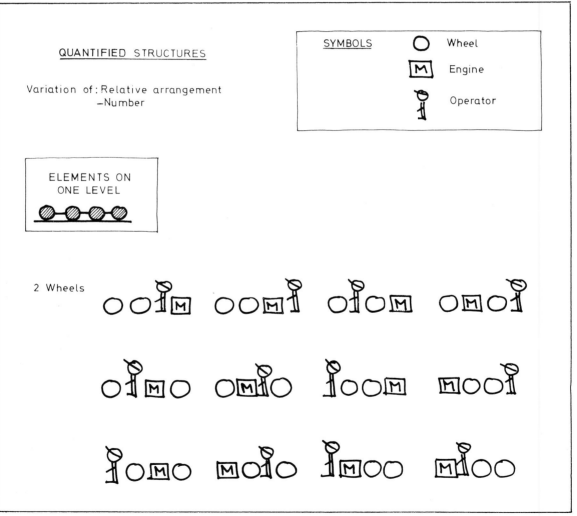

Figure 25   Quantified structures for road rollers

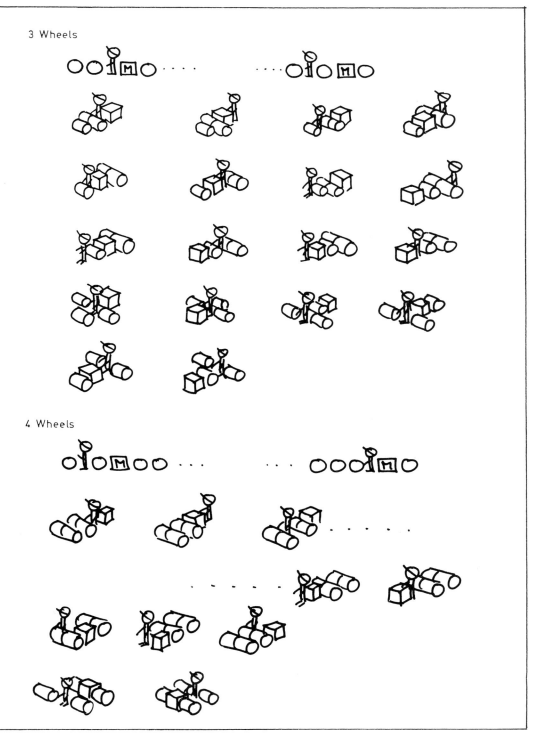

Figure 25 (continued)

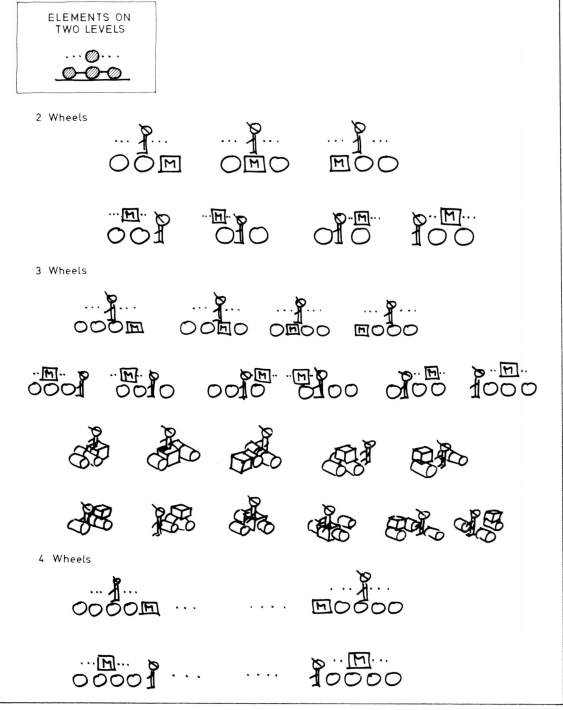

Figure 25 (continued)

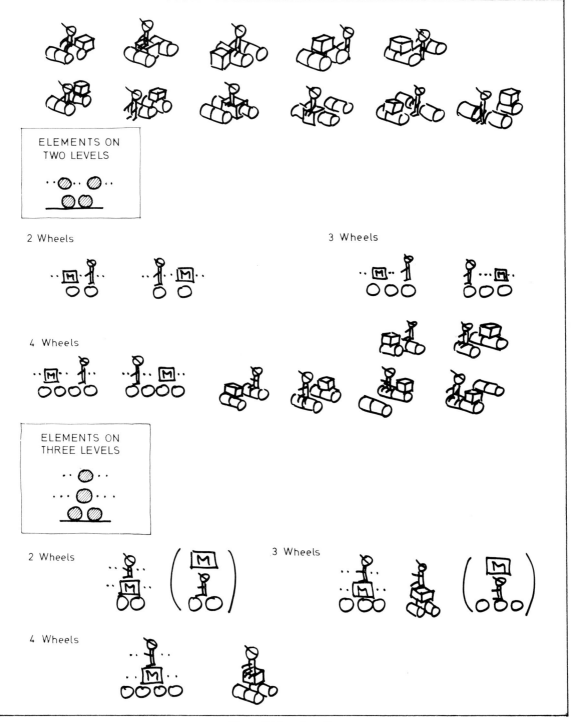

Figure 25 (continued)

figures express the levels on which the elements lie in relation to the earth. Of course an element (e.g. the engine) may lie on a level between the ones we are considering, but as the possibilities are obviously innumerable we begin by dividing the problem into a reasonable number (four, in this case) of categories. When a given structure is chosen for closer examination one must still feel free to vary the arrangement of the elements, although within narrow limits. Figure 26 shows some modern existing road rollers.

Figure 26   Road rollers. (See also Figure 25)

Figure 26 (continued)

Range of solutions for two and three elements

It is necessary to ask 'How many quantified structures is it realistic to draw up, and is it possible to get a clear view of the whole range of solution?' In many cases this can be done if only the most important elements are included as a basis for the variations. The possibilities for two and three elements are examined below.

If we examine the relative arrangement of two elements of approximately equal size we can draw up the possibilities shown in Figure 27. Obviously the angle of the two elements can be varied gradually, but the range of solutions can be illustrated by the angles shown.

The relative arrangement of three elements of the same order of size can be subjected to the same considerations. Figure 28 shows a number of possibilities at the shown level of detail. The great number of solutions that emerge through a permutation of three different elements in each of the positions shown will always be quickly limited when working on a specific product. An example of this is shown in the example on page 42.

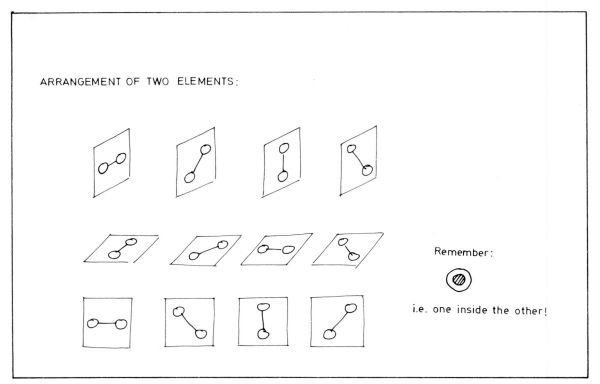

Figure 27   Possibilities for the relative arrangement of two elements

RELATIVE ARRANGEMENT OF THREE ELEMENTS

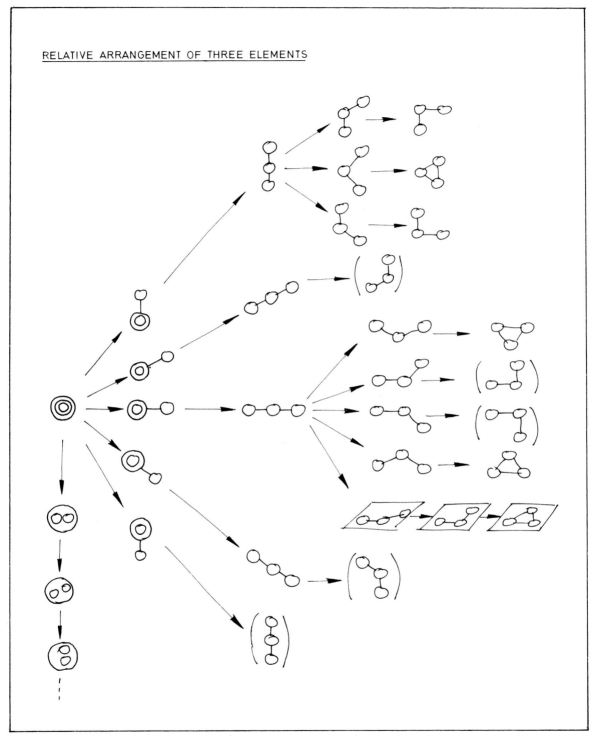

Figure 28   Possibilities for the relative arrangement of the three elements

Structure variation in connection with function

The functional connection between the most important elements is expressed in the basic structure, most
often in some sort of sketch showing the principle
of the design, where commonly accepted symbols
for known elements (machine, hydraulic, pneumatic,
electric symbols, etc) are used. So long as this sketch
expresses the basic structure it is exempt from any
definite dimensions or form, but it may be the
starting point for a series of quantified structures
built on the structure variation method with the
relative arrangement and dimensions as parameters
for each separate element in the basic structure.

Figure 29 shows the quantified structure for a
baling pump intended for keeping a moored boat
empty of water by the rocking movement of the
boat being used as the source of energy for the
pump. As the boat rocks, a pendulum on a vertical
axis swings from side to side and this drives a piston
pump. The inset of Figure 29 shows the basic
structure.

Figure 29 also illustrates the fact that there are
many possible variations, as the relative arrangement
and the dimensions can be changed continuously. It
is therefore important to make the variations at the
correct stage, which means that the number of elements considered must not be too great (less
important ones are kept for later), and that the
parameters must be varied in suitable steps. Thus
each suggested solution sketched must be thought
of as representing a category of solutions. Later,
when choosing the best suggestions, the individual
categories may be examined more closely.

QUANTIFIED STRUCTURES

Variation of: Relative arrangement
        – Dimensions

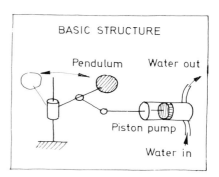

BASIC STRUCTURE

RELATIVE ARRANGEMENT

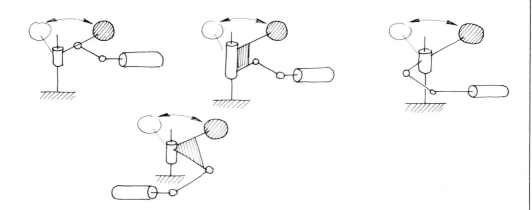

DIMENSIONS

to vary: A, B, L, D, V :

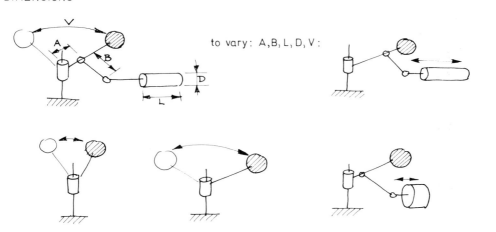

Figure 29   Quantified structures for a baling pump

Figure 30 shows a number of quantified structures for a gear, drawn up on the basis of the basic structure illustrated in the inset. Here the relative arrangement and the dimensions are not independently varied. Whether it is useful to keep the two parameters separate during the search for solutions depends on the nature of the problem, a fact which is also evident from the other examples in this section. Figure 31 shows examples of structure variation for a labelling machine. The top illustration shows quantified structures for four existing labelling machines, and a number of other possibilities are shown below. Finally, Figure 32 shows some quantified structures for an excavator, and Figure 33 demonstrates how three of these are employed in existing excavators.

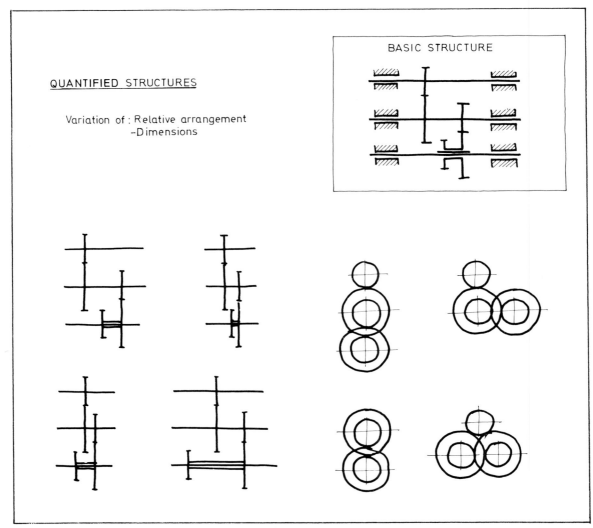

Figure 30   Quantified structures for a gear

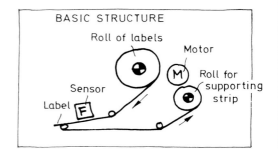

BASIC STRUCTURE

QUANTIFIED STRUCTURES

Variation of : Relative arrangement
　　　　　　 – Dimensions

4 existing labelling machines :

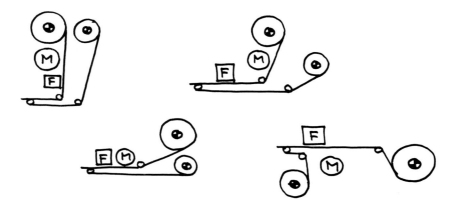

Other possibilities :

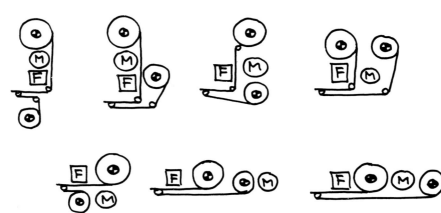

Figure 31　　Quantified structures for a labelling machine

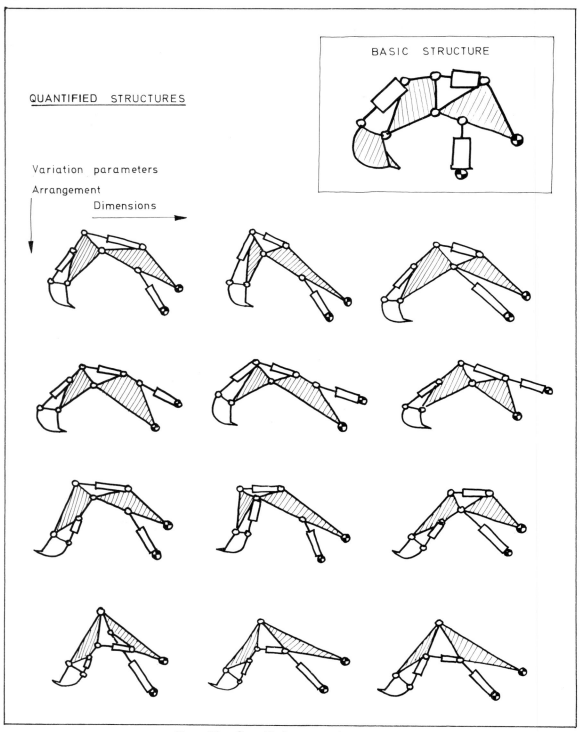

Figure 32   Quantified structures for an excavator

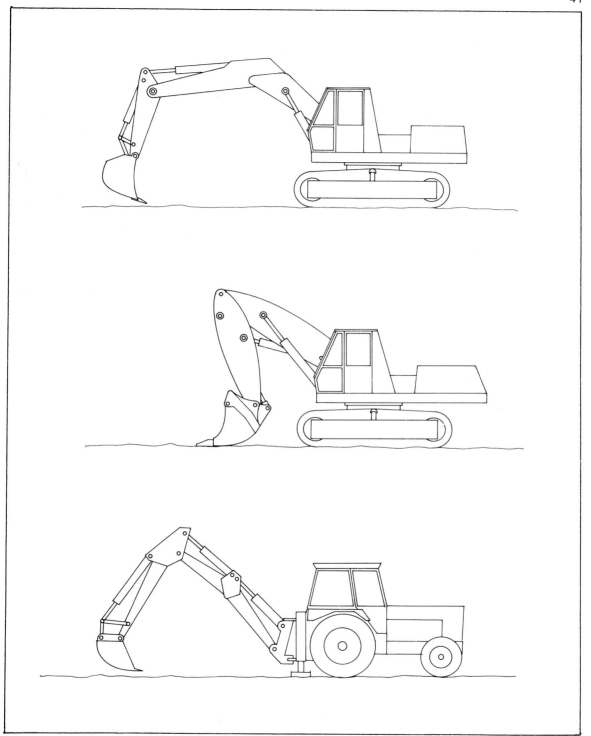

Figure 33   Excavators with different quantified structures. (See also Figure 32)

A coherent example: a tea-maker

In this section we will examine how the two structure variation methods can be employed successively. For example, consider a tea-maker, where boiling water is poured onto tea leaves, and where the tea brews before the leaves are removed from the finished tea. We imagine that we have reached a stage in the design work where different basic structures have been considered, so that the quantified structure must be considered.

As a first approach to the quantified structure we may look at the relative arrangement of the three main elements: a container for cold water, one for tea that is brewing, and finally one for the finished tea, where the latter may perhaps be a traditional teapot. The many possibilities illustrated in Figure 28 are reduced since structures which are symmetrical round a vertical axis are identical. The relative arrangements are shown in Figure 34. Note how the simple sketches contribute to making systematic variation easy. Variations can be made by drawing from one solution to another.

Among the solutions in Figure 34 are some which can be excluded on the basis of criteria such as handling (the teapot ought not to be inside the other containers) and questions of space (e.g. the three elements in a row can be omitted).

The next step in deciding on more detailed quantified structures consists of connecting the usable structures in Figure 34 with a basic structure which it is assumed has been chosen before the relative arrangement of the elements was considered. The inset in Figure 35 shows a rough sketch of a suggestion for a basic structure. The main illustration shows twenty different quantified structures expressing the relative arrangement of the elements and the functional relationship between them.

It is possible, in the light of the diagrams in Figure 35, to discard some structures. The factors that can be used as criteria are: price (complexity), appearance, handling and effectiveness. The final choice of structure can only be safely made after considering the design possibilities for some of the most promising structures.

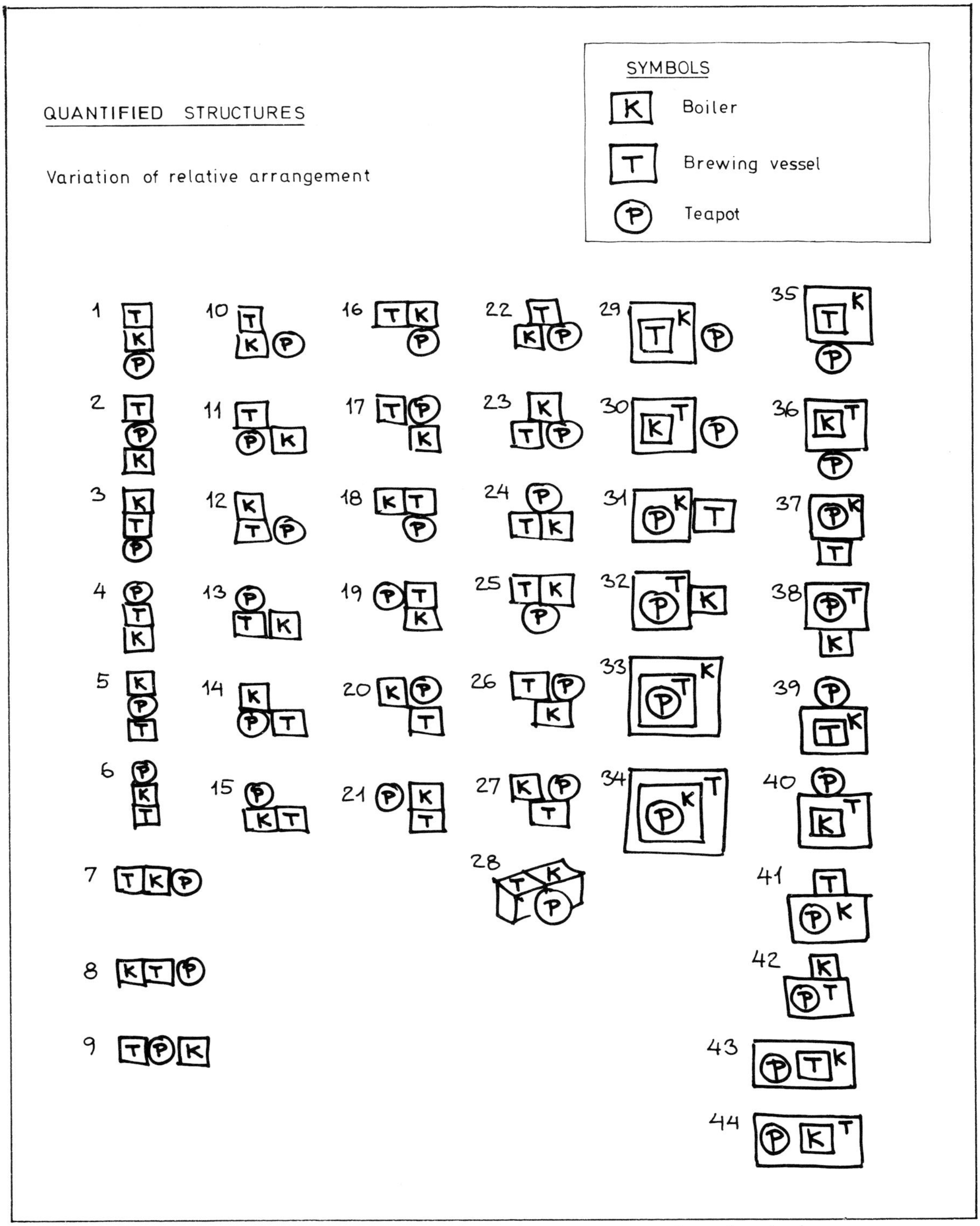

Figure 34   Relative arrangement of boiler, brewing vessel and teapot for design of the teamaker

QUANTIFIED STRUCTURES

Variation of relative arrangement

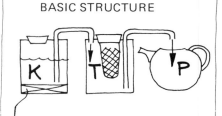

BASIC STRUCTURE

Heating element which forces the boiling water into the brewing vessel. After brewing, a remaining amount of water is boiled, whereby the tea is forced into the teapot

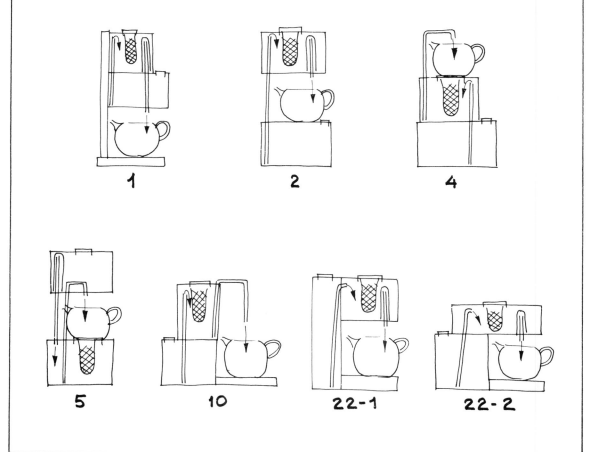

Figure 35   Basic structure and twenty quantified structures for an automatic teamaker. (The figures refer to Figure 34)

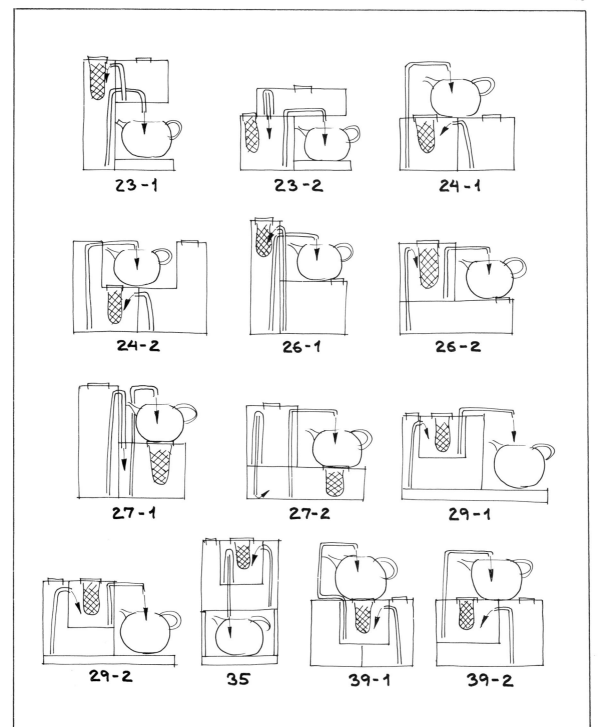

Figure 35 (continued)

Structure modelling

When varying the structure it is always necessary to visualise the possibilities. Diagrams with simplified symbols are suitable for this purpose. This can be seen from the previous examples in this section. Making three-dimensional models may, however, also be relevant. Figure 36 shows some structures for a tea maker modelled with simple toy bricks. (See also Figure 34).

Where more complex structures are being considered, sketches are not sufficient, and in such cases three-dimensional modelling is the only possibility. A typical three-dimensional model is shown in Figure 37, where quantified structures for a test tube filling machine are shown. (For a more detailed description of the machine see page 56). As the intention of such a model is to find out which relative arrangements of the elements are realistic, the model must be constructed in such a way that the elements can be quickly moved to new positions. For this purpose bricks of polystyrene are extremely useful, partly because they are easy to carve, and partly because their light weight allows a brick to be held fast in any position by just being pressed down onto a thin spike. Note here that we are talking about structure models and not about form models. This means that the component elements only need to be modelled by the space they will occupy and not by their form details. (See also chapter 5, which also deals with three-dimensional structure models).

Figure 36   Making three-dimensional models of quantified structures for a teamaker with the aid of toy bricks. (See also Figure 34)

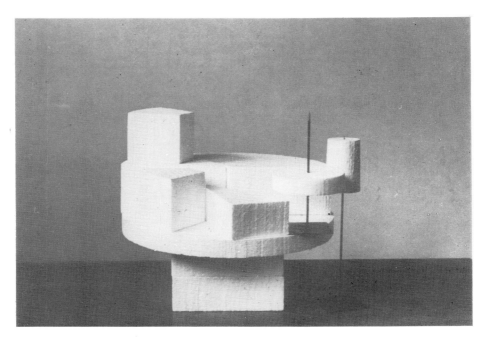

Figure 37   Three-dimensional models of quantified structures for a test tube filling machine. On an evaluation of space and
handling conditions the best structure may be chosen

2.3 Form variation

The idea of functional surfaces

In the previous section it was shown how the basis for the form design of a product is laid down by choosing the quantified structure. Once this choice has been made in a specific project the actual form design work can start. As the discussion of product synthesis showed, there are two aspects of the design that must be treated concurrently, namely the total form of the product and the form of the individual elements. The methods that may be employed for these two activities are broadly similar. So in the following pages, where we have used examples of element design, the methods demonstrated can be transferred directly to the total design and vice versa.

How can one make a start on the form design of a specific element? We must ask ourselves what it is that characterises the element in question. The element is a part of both a basic structure and of a quantified structure. We can therefore say that the element has been defined only by its function and by its functional relationship to its surroundings. The starting point of the form design must consequently be to formulate the functions the element must perform. Thereafter one can sketch the most important surfaces — or functional surfaces — and from these the rest of the element may be designed.

In this book a functional surface is taken to mean a surface that has an active function during use — for example, the slot in the head of a screw, the area of impact on the head of a hammer; the surface of a chair seat; the cogs on a wheel, etc.

We now examine the connection between the functional surfaces and the form. For example, let

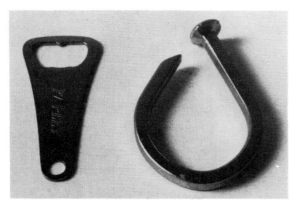

Figure 38   Two different bottle openers with apparently nothing in common

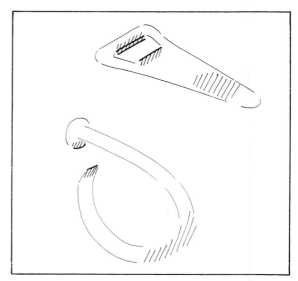

Figure 39   The functional surface for the two bottle openers

us select a simple element — a bottle opener. Figure 38 shows two types of opener which do not appear to have much in common; however, the functional surfaces are almost identical, see Figure 39. A bottle opener possesses three functional surfaces as shown. The difference between the two types illustrated consists in the different spacial arrangement of the material connecting the functional surfaces.

We can therefore identify two steps in the design of an element, on the one hand determining the functional surfaces and, on the other, deciding how these will be connected together. As already mentioned, Figure 39 shows this last step, while Figure 40 illustrates how other arrangements of the functional surfaces give rise to other form design possibilities.

Functional surfaces are the basis of the form design of any product. It is therefore appropriate to discuss in more detail what, in fact, functional surfaces are. In a product consisting of more than one element there are two types of functional surfaces — external and internal. External surfaces have an active function in relation to the surroundings, such as a handle, a supporting surface, etc. The internal surfaces have an active function in relation to other elements of the product.

This can be illustrated by imagining a product as a system consisting of a number of elements with certain relationships to each other. The vice in Figure 41 may thus be described as a system shown

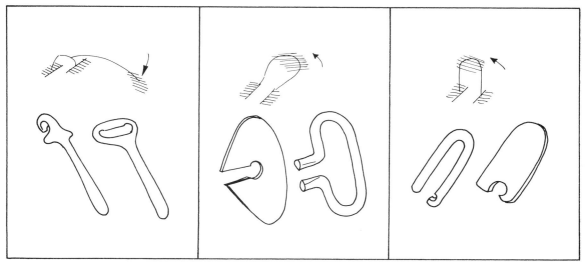

Figure 40   Different choices of functional surfaces give rise to different design possibilities

Figure 41   A vice. The starting point for Figures 42 to 44

in Figure 42, where the elements are represented by blocks and the relationship between them and the surroundings by lines.

If we consider a particular element of the vice e.g. the sliding jaw, we can see that the relations correspond exactly to the above mentioned functional surfaces. The sliding jaw has an external surface, consisting of the surface which presses on the subject as well as of the top horizontal surface. The internal surfaces consist of the hole for the spindle and the two holes for the rods. The functional surfaces are illustrated in Figure 43.

As shown in Figure 44, a specific arrangement of functional surfaces can be the basis for many form designs, and other arrangements can give other series of form designs. In the chapter on the form variation method we described the way in which the form design work can be tackled on the basis of functional surfaces. In the following paragraphs it will be apparent how a great deal of effort is needed to determine which functional surfaces are to be used in order that a firm and broad basis for the design work is achieved.

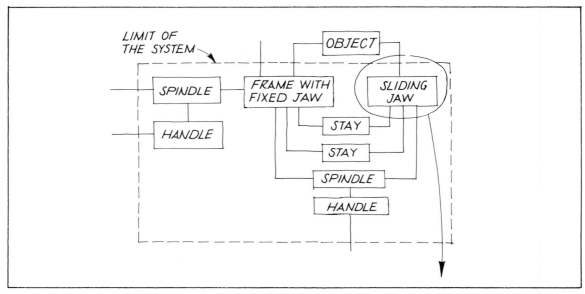

Figure 42   A vice. Relationship of elements

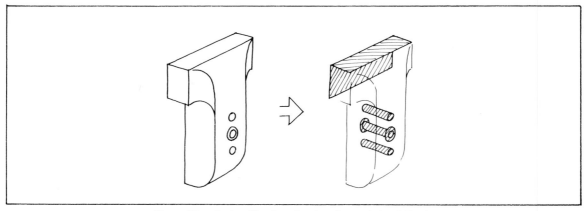

Figure 43   A vice. The functional surfaces of the sliding jaw

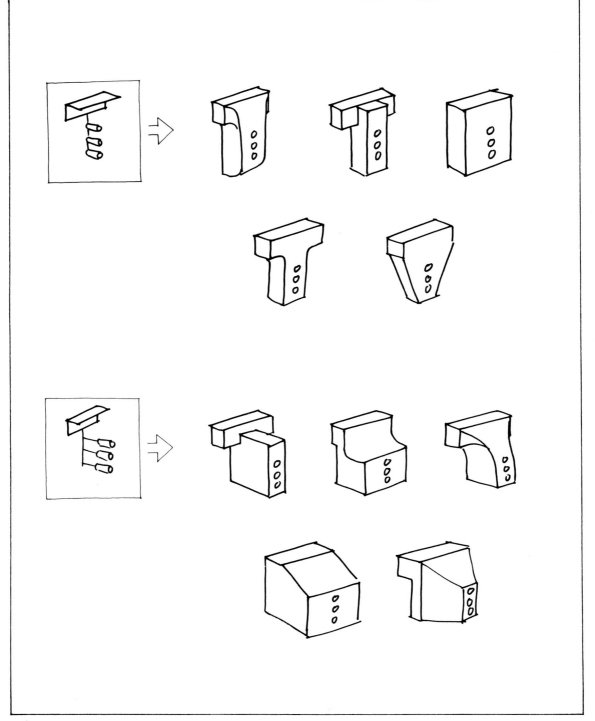

Figure 44   Suggested form designs for the sliding jaw, based on two different groups of the functional surfaces

The method of variation of the functional surfaces

A specification of the parameters that determine the functional surfaces of an element may form the basis of variation methods for generating ideas. By systematic variation of the parameters it becomes possible to list a number of arrangements of functional surfaces for a given element. The relevant parameters that can be varied are: number, arrangement, form geometry and dimension. Figures 45 and 46 show a number of examples of products, where the functional surfaces are emphasised. The products are presented in pairs in order that the four variation parameters may be observed, partly for the internal and partly for the external functional surfaces. As these are naturally a part of the final form we shall meet the four variation parameters again in connection with the later section on the form variation method.

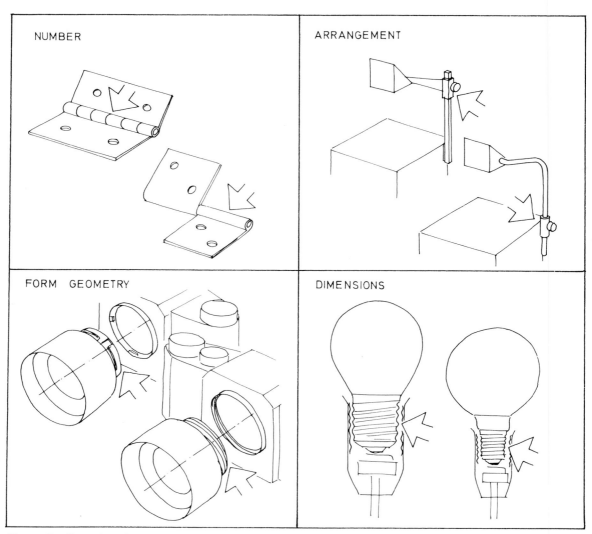

Figure 45   Examples of variation of internal functional surfaces based on the four variation parameters. The examples shown are — a hinge, overhead projector, a socket for a camera lens and a socket for an electric light bulb

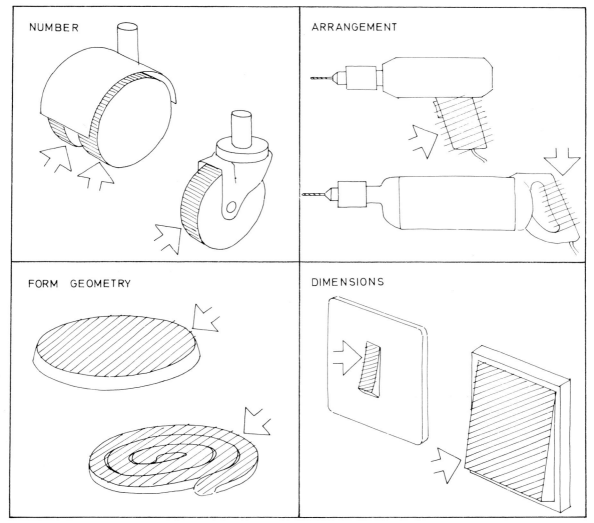

Figure 46 *Examples of variation of external functional surfaces based on the four variation parameters. The examples are — a wheel for a chair, an electric drill, a hotplate and an electric switch*

54

FUNCTIONAL SURFACES

Variation parameters :
        - Number
        - Arrangement
        - Dimension
        - Form geometry

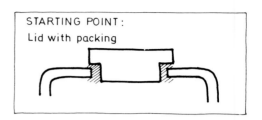

STARTING POINT :
Lid with packing

NUMBER

ARRANGEMENT

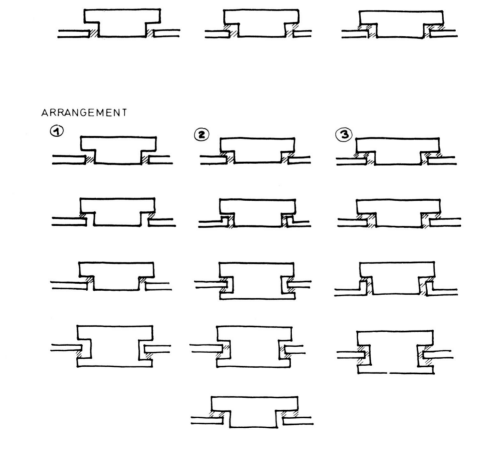

Figure 47   Variation of functional surfaces for a lid with packing — number, arrangement

In the following paragraphs it will be shown how variation of the functional surfaces may be applied in a particular problem. This is to design an area of packing round a lid, cover, cork or similar object. The problem is illustrated in Figure 47 (inset). An examination of the problem on the basis of varying the four variation parameters may, for instance, give the suggestions shown in Figures 47 and 48. These must not be regarded as final suggestions, but only as categories of solutions, as each of the suggestions shown must be further elaborated at the detail design stage.

The variation parameters may generally be freely varied inside the limits where the functional surfaces can fulfill their function. If the full range of solutions is to be thoroughly examined it will be necessary to evaluate the limits for the individual paramaters.

As an overall check on the limits it may be useful to examine the functional surfaces with the greatest extent and those with the smallest extent. Such surfaces may be suitably called maximum and minimum surfaces, see Figure 49.

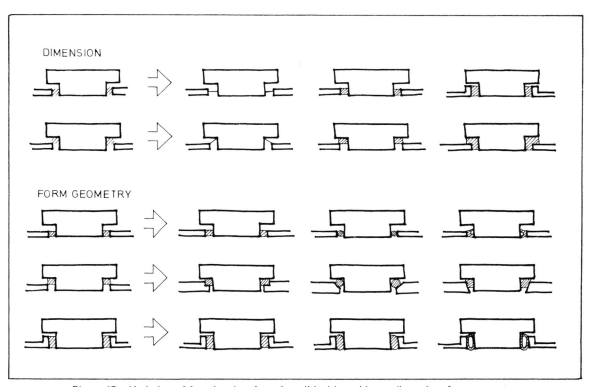

Figure 48   Variation of functional surfaces for a lid with packing — dimension, form geometry

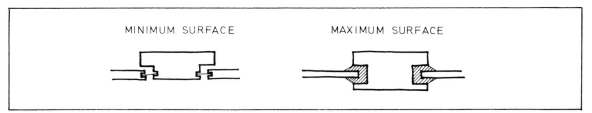

Figure 49   Minimum and maximum functional surface for a lid with packing

It is, of course, a personal matter whether one decides to apply the variation principles systematically, or whether one simply uses maximum and minimum surfaces supplemented by a few possibilities in between. In any case, a knowledge of the variation of number, arrangement, form geometry and dimension is important, whether it is applied consciously or is simply part of the attitude with which one attacks a given task. Let us therefore consider some details in a specific machine on the basis of a more flexible attitude, while primarily studying maximum and minimum surfaces.

Figure 50 shows a machine that can carry out a number of processes with test tubes in connection with nutrients for tests on bacteria. The processes that the test tubes go through are: sterilisation (by heat), cooling, filling with nutrient, closing with a sterile wad of cotton wool and labelling. The tubes are loaded manually, transported through the machine on a continuous circular conveyor and taken out by hand.

The conveyor's functional surfaces must form a support so that the tubes cannot fall over. A maximum surface is easy to define, namely a hole with a round bottom, which can completely surround the test tube. A minimum surface is theoretically three points supporting the table, but as the tube must not be able to fall over by accident, it must be supported on at least five or six points. The design of the conveyor is shown in Figure 51. It is constructed so that the tubes are supported at five points by the conveyor and at a sixth one, below, by a fixed table top over which the tubes slide. Minimum surfaces for the conveyor have been chosen in this case because the conveyor, as well as the test tubes, goes through both the heater and the cooling zone and so the heat capacity of the conveyor needs to be kept to a minimum.

The loading system is a funnel-shaped magazine which can take thirty test tubes. The tubes are passed along by being grasped one at a time by a drum, whereupon they are swung down into the circular

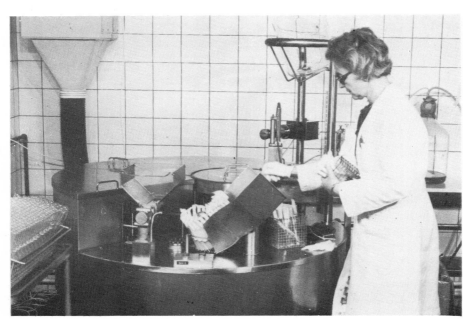

Figure 50   Machine for filling test tubes. This machine carries out automatic sterilisation, filling with the correct dose, corking and labelling of test tubes (Inst. for Product Development, The Technical University of Denmark)

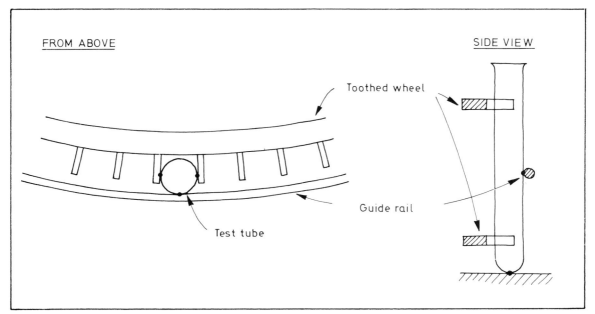

FROM ABOVE

SIDE VIEW

Toothed wheel

Guide rail

Test tube

Figure 51   The functional surfaces in the circular conveyor in the test tube machine are designed as minimum surfaces

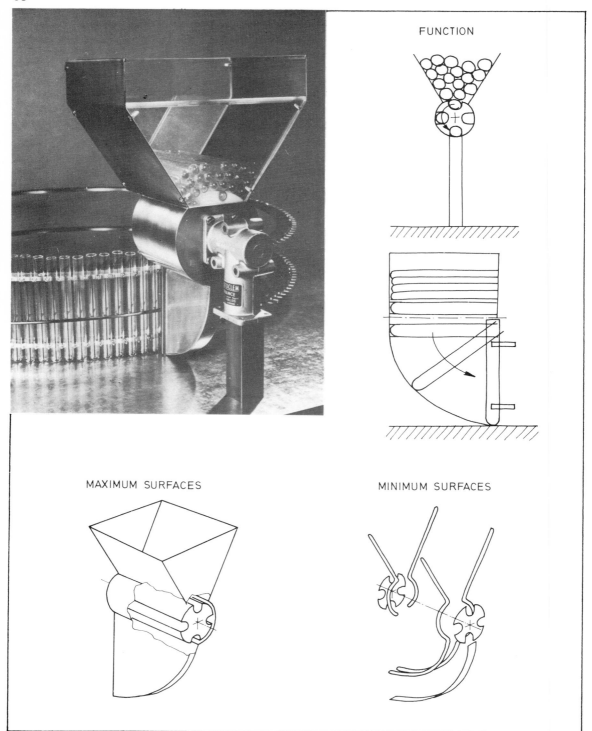

FUNCTION

MAXIMUM SURFACES

MINIMUM SURFACES

Figure 52   Loading system for the test tube filling machine. The actual design as well as other functional surfaces are shown

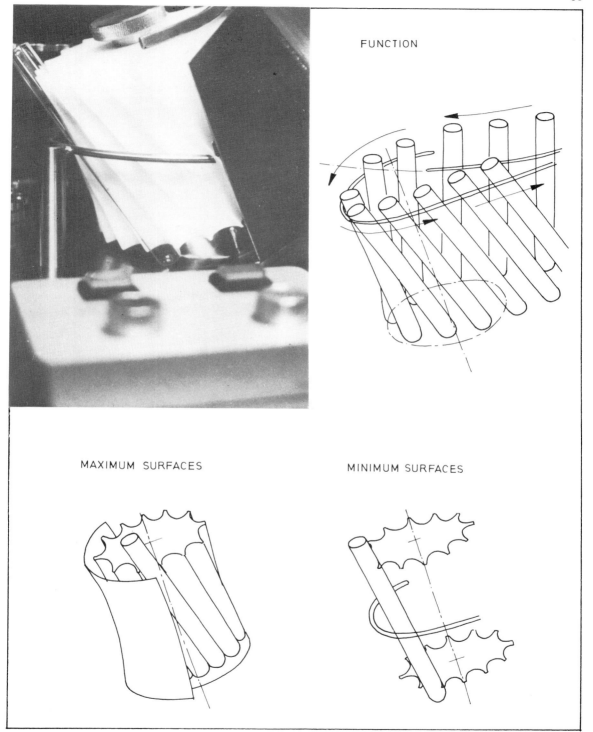

FUNCTION

MAXIMUM SURFACES

MINIMUM SURFACES

Figure 53   Unloading system of the test tube filling machine

conveyor as shown in Figure 52. If the loading system is constructed using maximum surfaces the tubes must be supported and guided as much as possible. The result can be seen at the bottom left in Figure 52. To design the functional surfaces as minimum ones, the desired function may be achieved as long as the tubes are constantly supported at four points, see Figure 52, bottom right. In the machine, the loading system is designed using maximum surfaces to prevent damage to the tubes and to prevent the operator getting his fingers trapped.

When, after the cycle is completed, the test tubes leave the circular conveyor they are grasped by a drum which passes them up into a magazine, where the operator can remove them. The operation of the unloading drum is illustrated in Figure 53, top. The drum rotates on a sloping axis, so that the test tubes are moved in a hyperboloid plane. When the tubes have completed a half circuit they are forced up into the magazine. If maximum surfaces are used for the drum, we get a design like the one bottom left in Figure 53. A minimum surface will be completely analogous to the circular conveyor in Figure 54, as it is sufficient to have two points of contact above and two below as well as a point in the middle and one at the bottom. In the machine, the drum is designed with functional surfaces close to the maximum. Here again, the main reason is to prevent damage to the test tubes.

Restrictions on form design

Let us imagine that we have a proposal for the form design of the functional surfaces of an element. How then do we move on from there? As has already been mentioned, the functional surfaces must be connected together. The problem is now to arrange the connections so that the element can function in use. The role of the element when in use must therefore be assessed and taken into consideration.

The conditions that may have to be taken account of in the form design of an element can be formulated as follows:

Banned areas:

1. Areas in space which are structurally conditioned must not be obstructed, i.e. other elements must not be hampered (this applies to both stationary and movable elements).
2. Areas in space which are functionally conditioned must not be obstructed, (e.g. the objects in the process, rays of light and jets of water).
3. Areas in space which are operationally conditioned must not be obstructed (e.g. room for a hand, room for an operator, etc).

On the basis of these banned areas one can now draw up a number of form design suggestions that roughly show where in space the connections must be put. The next step is to decide on the form geometry and the dimensions — first as rough sketches and, thereafter, in detail drawings, judged on for instance technological or aesthetic criteria (see also Chapter 3).

It is important to note from the preceding comments that the form design of an element contains both a qualitative and a quantitative part. Any decision on dimensions is irrelevant until it has been decided how the material will be arranged, e.g. whether a functional surface will be supported at one point or at several. The number of elements and the relative arrangement of the connections belong to the qualitative part of the form design, while geometry and dimension belong to the quantitative one. The following section explains how the variation of parameters can be applied.

The form variation method

The variation parameters: number, arrangement form geometry and dimension, are general form parameters, and we have already shown how these may be used in the search for possible functional surfaces. The interaction of the four parameters with the form of the material that connects the functional surfaces is illustrated in Figures 54 and 55.

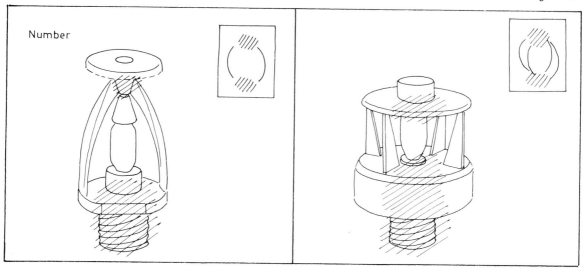

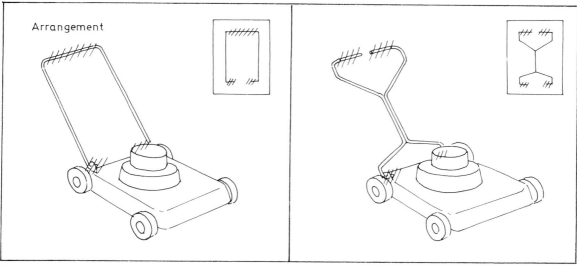

Figure 54 The variation parameters of number and arrangement can be used in connection with arranging the material area to connect the functional surfaces. The examples show two sprinkler valves and two motor lawn mowers

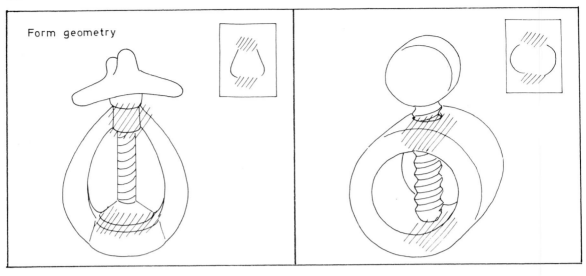

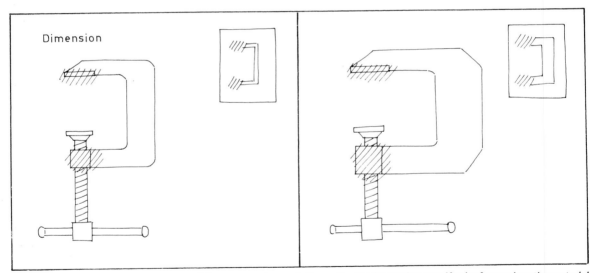

Figure 55 *The variation parameters of form geometry and dimension can be used to specify the form when the material area (see Figure 54) has been chosen. The examples show two nutcrackers and two clamps*

Taking a typical example — the frame in a hydraulic press — we now observe how the variation parameters can be used in designing an element. The frame of the press contains two functional surfaces, namely the fastening areas for respectively the hydraulic cylinder and the pressure plate, see Figure 56. When designing the frame there are three banned areas:

1. There must be room for the piston in all its positions;
2. There must be room for an object of a closely defined maximum size;
3. There must be room for the object to be put into and taken out of the press.

In other words the frame must be designed so that the two function surfaces are connected in a way which takes account of the banned areas, and which allows it to fulfill its function — to transmit the necessary forces.

Figure 57 shows how the variation of number and arrangement of elements may be used to examine where the material can lie. After that, the variation of form geometry and dimension make it possible to detail a number of rough design suggestions or form concepts.

For comparison, Figure 58 shows the design of a number of existing presses.

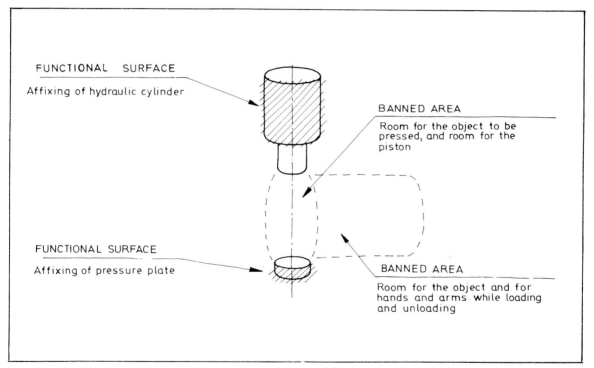

Figure 56   Functional surfaces and banned areas in connection with the form design of a frame for a hydraulic press

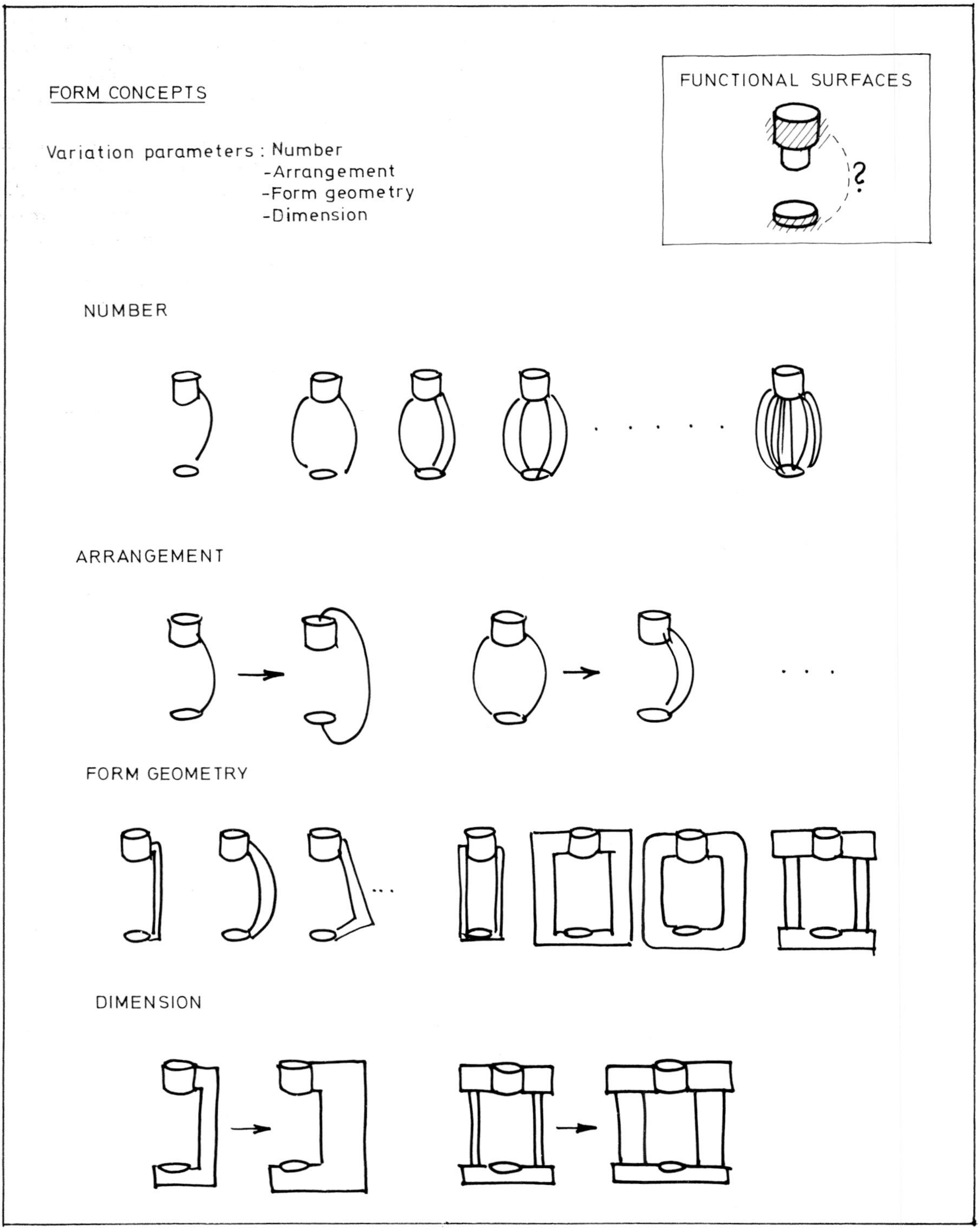

64

FORM CONCEPTS

Variation parameters : Number
                   -Arrangement
                   -Form geometry
                   -Dimension

FUNCTIONAL SURFACES

NUMBER

ARRANGEMENT

FORM GEOMETRY

DIMENSION

Figure 57   Form concepts for a frame for a hydraulic press

Figure 58   Hydraulic press. See also Figure 57

A more detailed use of the variation parameters is possible through a closer indication of the material areas between the function surfaces. This is illustrated in the following example.

Figure 59 shows the functional surfaces in a fork joint with a single bearing at one end and double bearings at the other. In varying the material area it is appropriate to use three sorts of symbols; a line for something that is approximately a rod (straight or curved), a hatched plane for something flat, and finally a hatched area for something solid, i.e. material in three dimensions. Variation of form geometry and dimension can result in a series of form proposals as shown in Figure 60. Note that it is useful to work at two levels of abstraction, namely, with a series of solutions where number and arrangement are varied (Figure 59) and one where form geometry and dimension are varied (Figure 60). Note also the considerable difference in illustration technique.

The form proposals must now be further detailed, and it becomes necessary to take into consideration the form factors (see p. 98) that actually exist. In the example of the fork joint, the manufacturing process becomes a decisive factor for the choice of design, compare Figures 60 and 98.

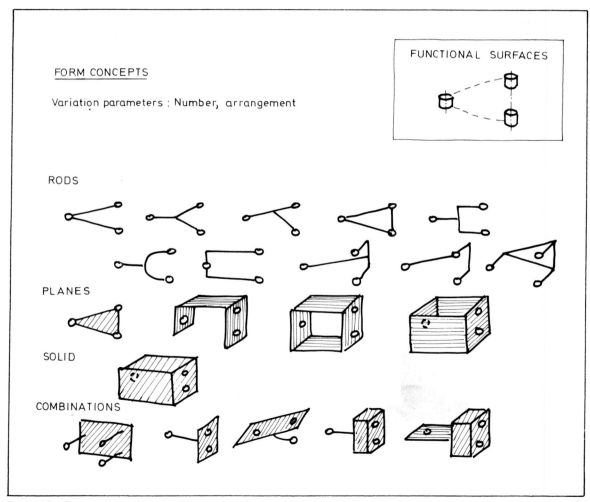

Figure 59   Form concepts for a fork joint at the most abstract level, where the number and arrangement of the material areas are examined

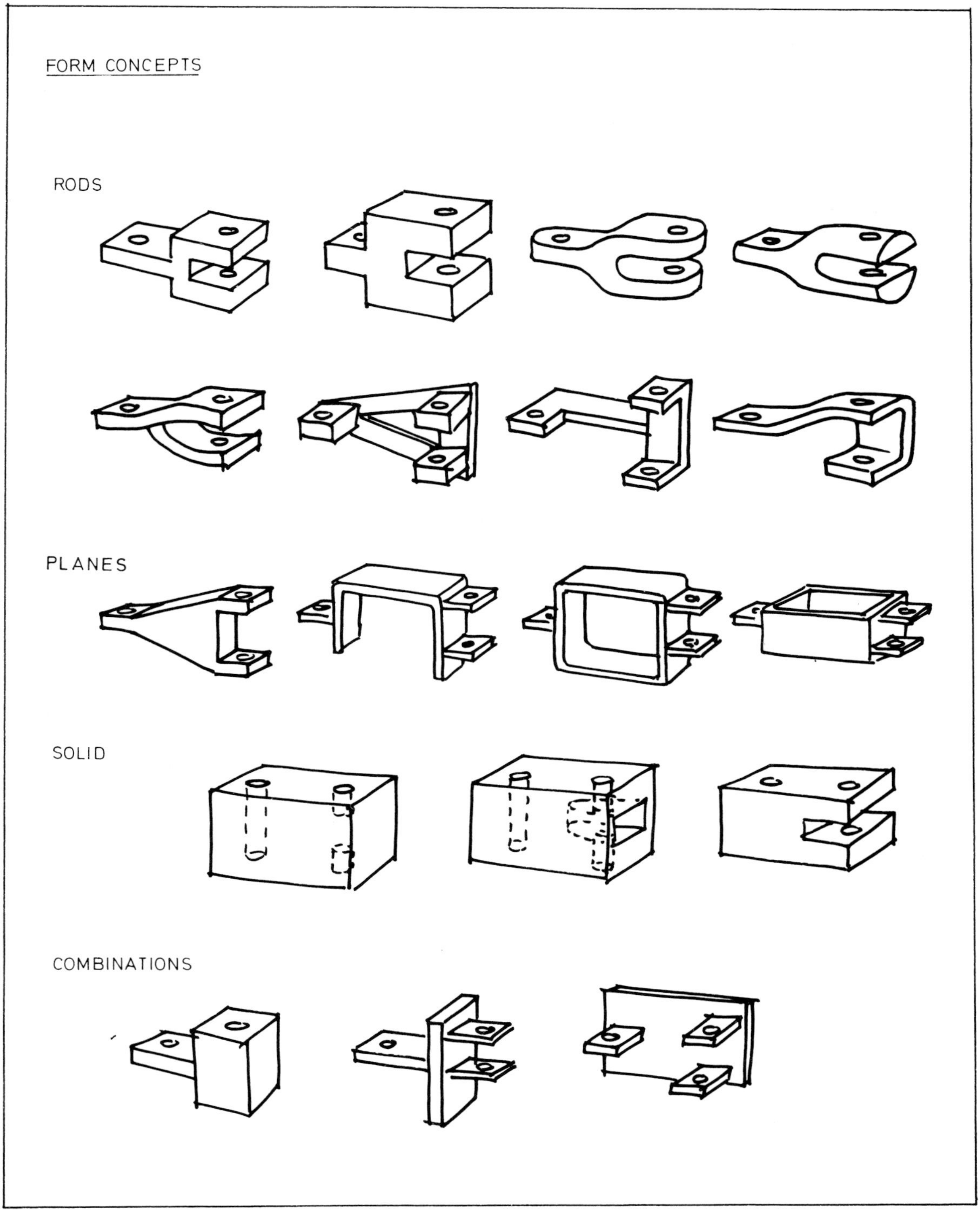

FORM CONCEPTS

RODS

PLANES

SOLID

COMBINATIONS

Figure 60   Form concepts for a fork joint drawn up on the basis of Figure 59 and variation of form geometry and dimension. (See also Figure 98)

Finally the form variation method will be illustrated by a slightly more complex example, a microscope. We have already studied the quantified structure for a microscope designed on the traditional principle, see Figure 23.

If the tube is made vertical or slightly slanting the conditions for the design of the frame may be illustrated as shown in Figure 61. The most important functional surfaces of the frame are surfaces for fixing the tube, the stage, the adjusting knob and the mirror as well as the supporting base. The banned areas are the tube, the stage, the adjusting knob, the mirror and the table top as well as the rays from the light source through the mirror to the object and on to the tube. There are also banned areas over the tube (where the operator is looking) and opposite the stage and the adjusting knob (where the operator's hands must have room to work.)

When the above conditions are fulfilled the frame material may be arranged freely in space and Figure 62 shows a number of suggested form designs drawn up by varying the number of elements and arrangement. A division into rods, planes and solid shapes has been made, as in the previous example. Note that for some of the parameters one can consider maximum and minimum values. Figure 63 shows form concepts arising out of variation of the form geometry and the dimension.

In Figure 62 and 63 it can be seen that variation of number and arrangement can be carried out quite systematically, while it is unrealistic to work systematically when varying form geometry and dimension. Here the most appropriate course is to combine the suggestions arising from varying number and arrangement with different basic geometric shapes and use this as a source of ideas for form suggestions. Figure 64 shows a series of existing microscopes.

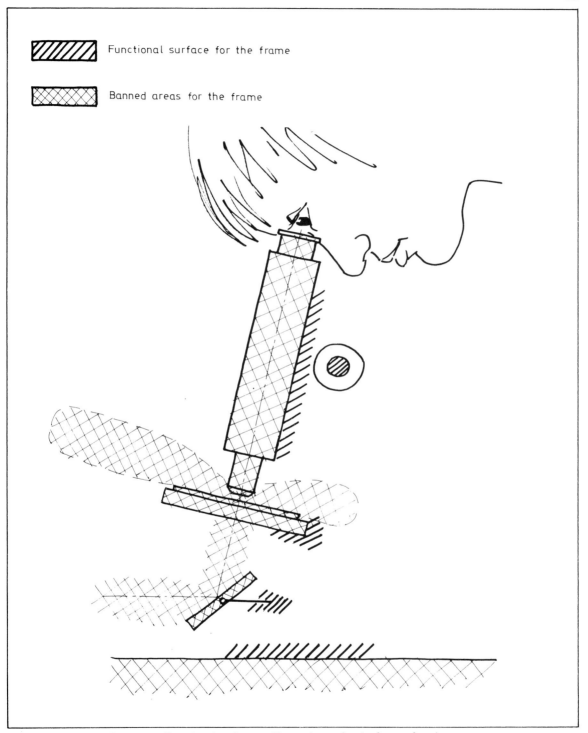

Functional surface for the frame

Banned areas for the frame

Figure 61   Functional surfaces and banned areas for the frame of a microscope

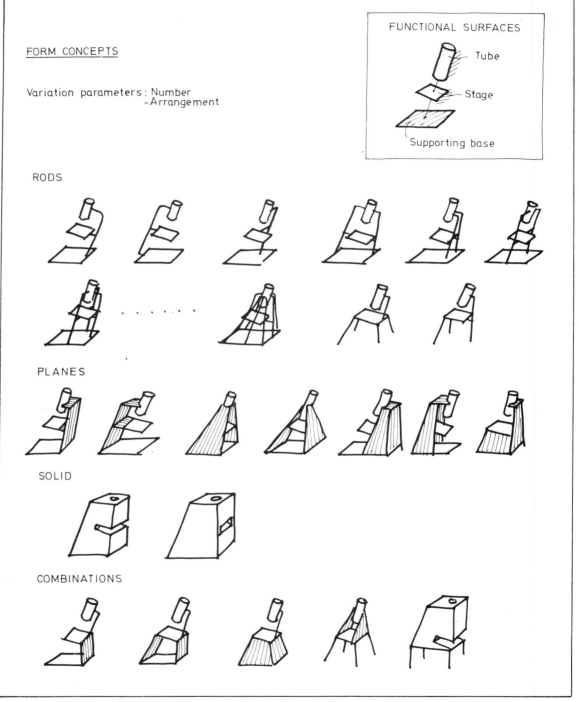

FORM CONCEPTS

Variation parameters: Number
                     -Arrangement

FUNCTIONAL SURFACES

Tube

Stage

Supporting base

RODS

PLANES

SOLID

COMBINATIONS

Figure 62   Form concepts for the frame of a microscope

FORM CONCEPTS

Variation parameters: Form geometry, dimension

RODS

PLANES

SOLID

COMBINATIONS

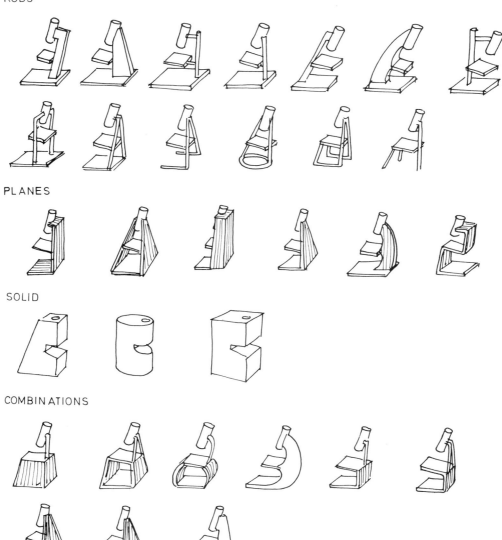

Figure 63   Form concepts for the frame of a microscope

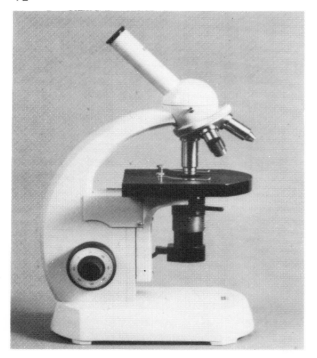
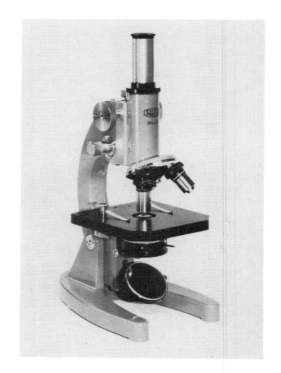

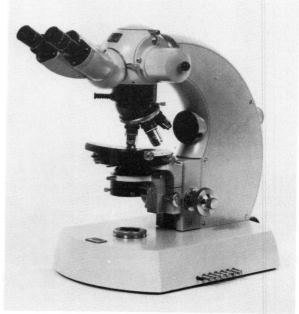

Figure 64   Various types of microscope (See also Figures 62 and 63). (Courtesy of Olympus, Carl Zeiss, Carl Zeiss JENA, Leitz, Ealing Beck, Vickers)

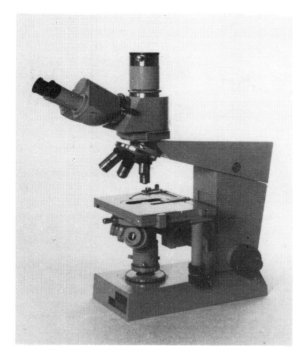

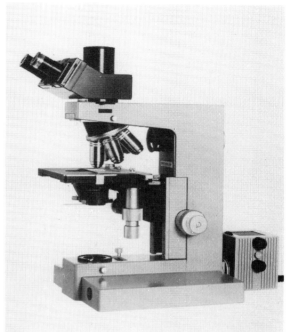

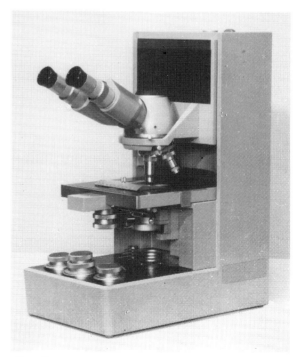

Figure 64 (continued)

The form division method

If the examples in the previous section are studied closely one more parameter can be identified. This, through conscious variation, can give rise to ideas for a number of suggestions for the design. If the microscopes in Figure 64 are compared it is obvious that one microscope frame consists of more elements than another.

This choice of dividing into more elements or integrating into a few is a choice which is always available. The division need not lead to more physically separate elements, as it may be caused by a visual division of a physically whole element. Figure 65 illustrates the points of view from which a product or a machine may be divided into elements. Firstly, the division may be done for reasons of function, secondly for physical reasons, i.e. whether the elements can be separated from each other, and thirdly for visual reasons.

A deliberate variation of the number of elements may be suitably called the form division method, bearing in mind that it may be a question of a division into more elements as well as an integration into a few — possibly into a single whole one.

In the examples on the following pages the physical and the visual divisions are considered. Incidentally it is not stated whether the elements are physically separable or not, as either type may be possible when a specific design is considered.

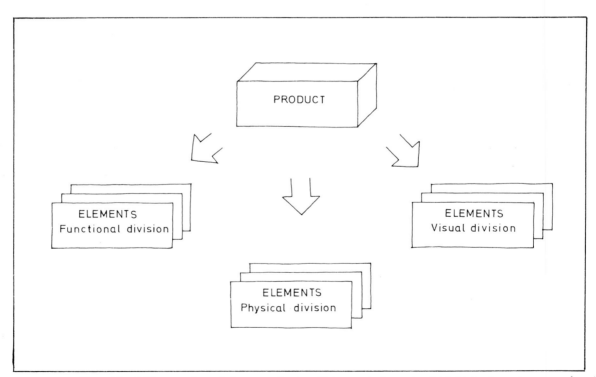

Figure 65   Different points of view according to which a product may be divided into elements

Figure 66 shows a pawl with four functional surfaces, — the area of the breaking function, the area of the bearing, the area of finger pressure and the area of pressure for a mechanical system, which must be moved simultaneously with the pawl being released. If it is assumed that the pawl must be form designed approximately as shown in the illustration, that is to say that the material areas are laid down, the form division method may give rise to the form design proposals shown. Note that the number of part elements goes from 1 (complete integration) to 5. It must be emphasised that the form division has no functional importance, but it may be very important for the manufacturing process and so for the economics.

In Figure 66 pawl 4 will be the cheapest one if only one is to be made, whereas pawl 1 may be cheapest in mass production.

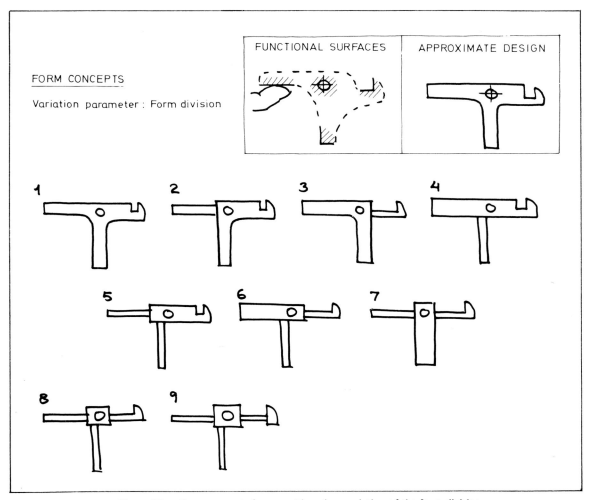

Figure 66   Form concepts for a pawl based on variation of the form division

We will now demonstrate the application of the form division method on an element by one more example. The bearing in Figure 67 contains two areas of bearing and a supporting surface, and the approximate form design is shown. The rest of the figure contains a number of ideas to which the form division method gives rise. Here again, an essential factor in the choice of form design will be the manufacturing process.

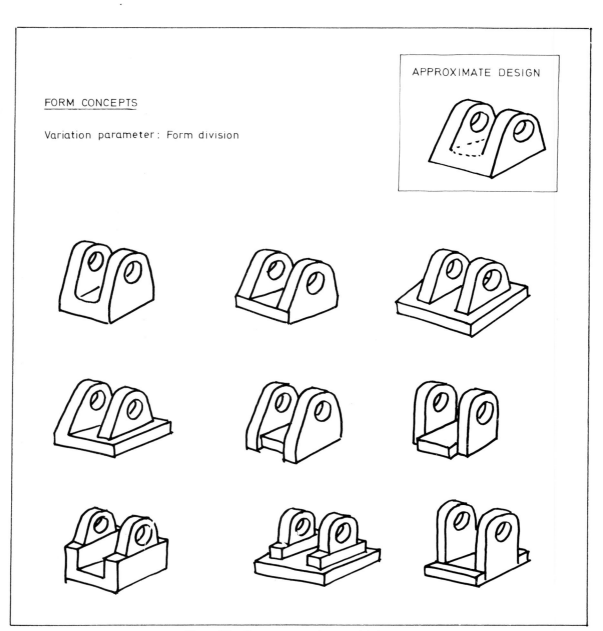

Figure 67   Form concepts for a double bearing

In the introduction to this chapter, it was mentioned that the methods in question may be used in designing either elements or complete products. This also applies to the form division method.

As an example let us study the tea maker in Figure 35. It is assumed that we will examine the forms that are possible if box shaped containers are chosen, placed side by side as shown in the inset in Figure 68. (In the same way other shapes of container may be examined). In the illustration a number of possibilities are illustrated for division or integration of the three elements comprising boiler, brewing vessel and plinth.

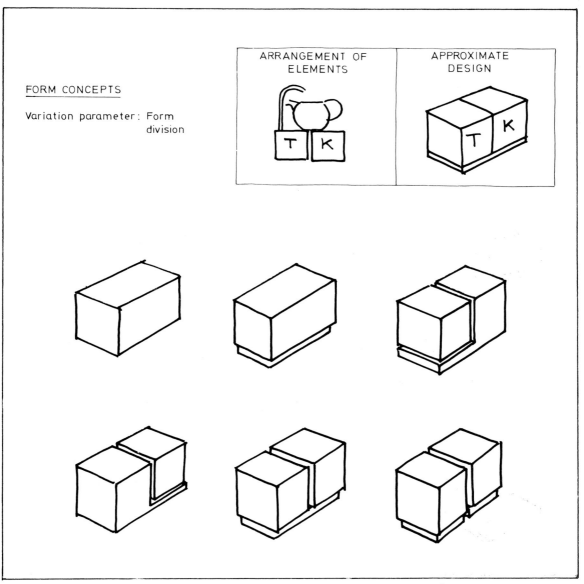

FORM CONCEPTS

Variation parameter: Form
                     division

ARRANGEMENT OF
ELEMENTS

APPROXIMATE
DESIGN

Figure 68   Form concepts for a teamaker. (See also Figure 35)

A more flexible application of the form division method is shown in Figure 69, where a calculator is being considered. The possibilities for variation are numerous, as any plane whatsoever can be integrated into or separated from the other planes. The criteria for deciding the choice of form design will be the manufacturing process, the appearance, cleaning, etc. (see also Chapter 3 'Form factors'). A number of calculators are shown, for comparison, in Figures 70 and 71.

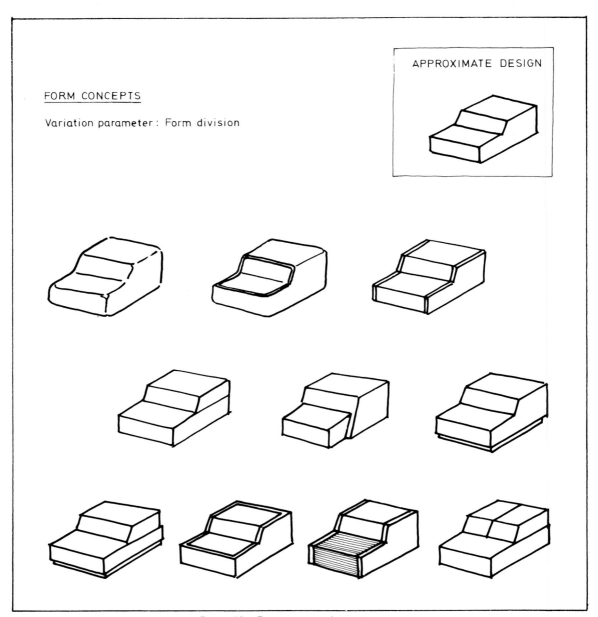

APPROXIMATE DESIGN

FORM CONCEPTS

Variation parameter : Form division

Figure 69   Form concepts for a calculator

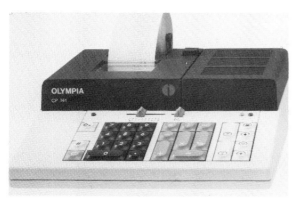

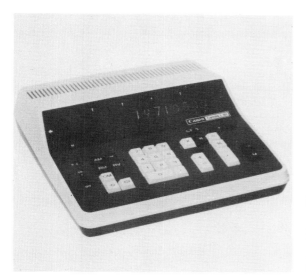

Figure 70   Types of calculator. (See also Figures 69 and 71). (Courtesy of Olympia, .Facit and Cannon)

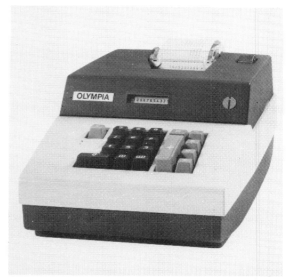

Figure 71   Types of calculator. (See also Figures 69 and 70). (Courtesy of Olympia, Diehl and Facit)

If it is carried out with imagination, variation of the form division may for a given product produce many different and exciting designs. It will therefore be useful to show a number of examples of products presented in pairs, so that the difference in form division for the individual products may be noted, (see Figures 72 to 76). It is obvious from the examples that a change in the form division may occasionally cause a radical alteration of a well-known product.

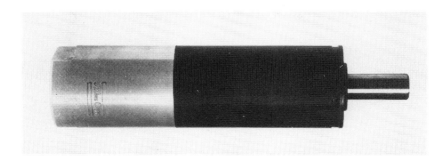

Figure 72   Pneumatic motors with a different form division, (Atlas Copco Ltd.)

Figure 73   Motor bicycles with different form division

Figure 74   Watering cans with different form division

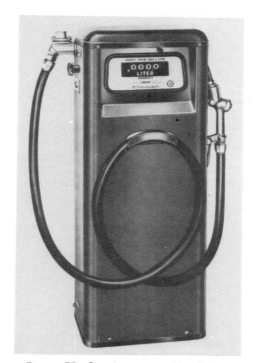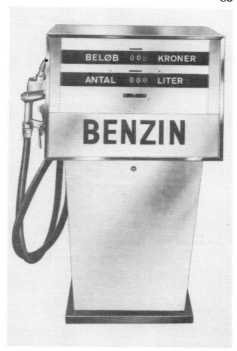

Figure 75 Petrol pumps with different form division. (Danish Industrial Syndicate Ltd.)

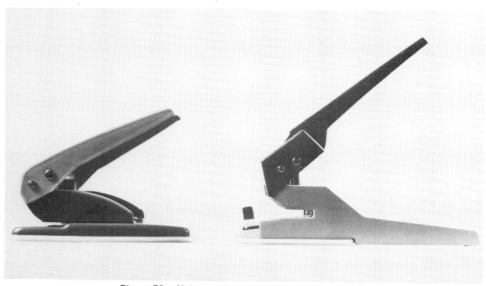

Figure 76 Hole punches with different form division

A coherent example: a pulley

It is usually appropriate to vary the five form variation parameters in the following order: number and arrangement; form geometry and dimension; form division. It is, however, not certain that in a given situation all five parameters can be used. For instance, the arrangement of a material area may be ruled by so many conditions that there is only one place for it. Alternatively, form geometry may be decided in advance. But this takes us on to the criteria and conditions that apply in a specific situation, which is the subject of Chapter 3. An example of the general situation, where all five variation parameters can be used, is shown below.

The object to be examined is a pulley, e.g. a conveyor belt. The pulley has two functional surfaces, the rolling surface and the bearings.

Variation of functional surfaces has been carried out in Figure 77, where four variation parameters as well as maximum and minimum surfaces are illustrated. Two groupings of functional surfaces have been chosen for further examination, and in Figure 78 possible material areas are shown based on a variation of numbers and relative arrangement. A division of the material areas into the form of rods, planes or solids is useful. Figure 79 shows how, by varying the form geometry and the dimension, a number of more specific form design ideas can be given. Possible form divisions for a few of these ideas are shown in Figure 80.

The final decision on the form depends largely on the choice of material and manufacturing process (see section 3.4) and possibly also on an evaluation of the appearance. By using sketches, models and scale drawings one can decide on all the details, which are then documented in a set of working drawings with the accompanying assembly drawing. Naturally this plan, which corresponds to Figures 77 to 80, is very schematic. This is in order to underline the steps one must basically take in designing. A more relaxed attitude to this will probably be more realistic, as can also be seen from the case history in Chapter 5.

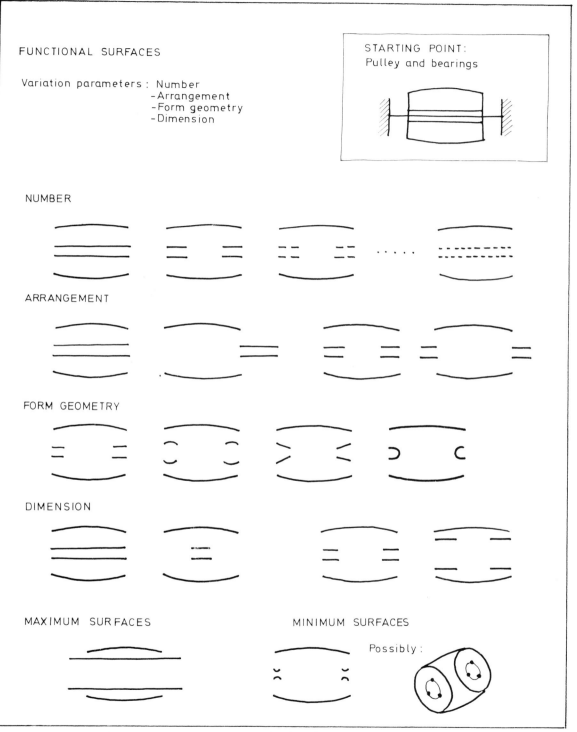

Figure 77   Variation of functional surfaces for a pulley on a conveyor belt

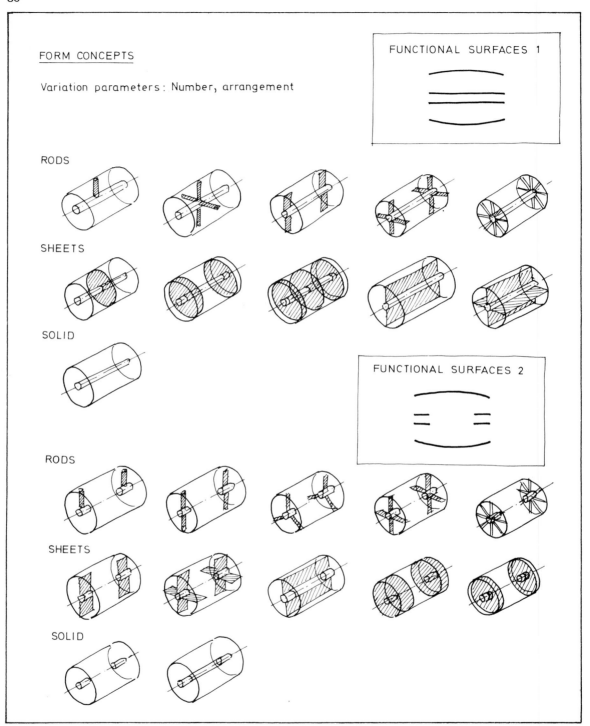

FORM CONCEPTS

Variation parameters: Number, arrangement

FUNCTIONAL SURFACES 1

RODS

SHEETS

SOLID

FUNCTIONAL SURFACES 2

RODS

SHEETS

SOLID

Figure 78   Form concepts for a pulley at the most abstract level, where the number and arrangement of the material areas are examined

FORM CONCEPTS

Variation parameters : Form geometry, dimension

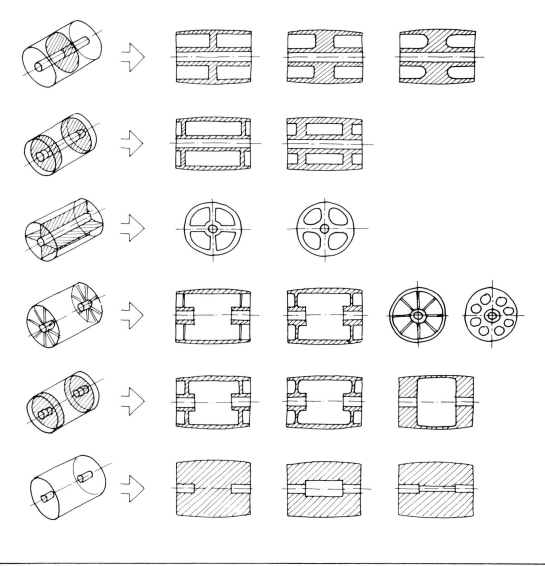

Figure 79   Form concepts for a pulley arrived at by varying the form geometry and dimension of selected solutions from
Figure 78

FORM CONCEPTS

Variation parameter: Form division

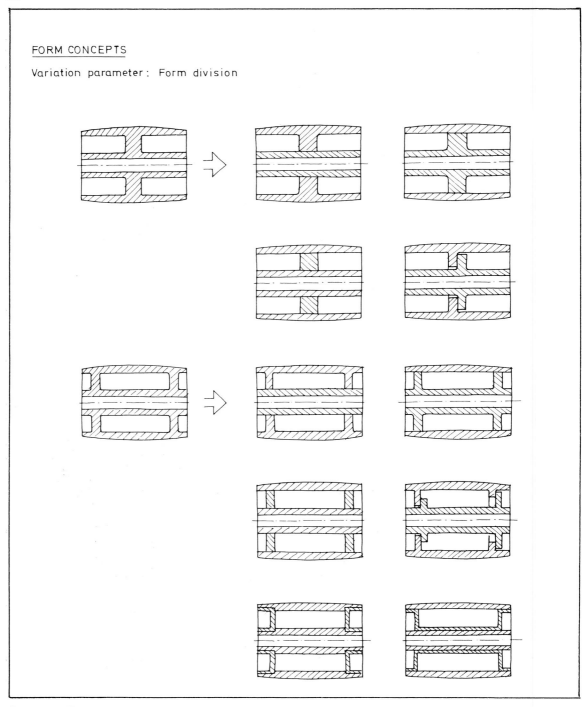

Figure 80   Form concepts for a pulley. Two of the suggested solutions in Figure 79 have been detailed to a certain level by varying the form division. For the final detailed design the design engineer must first decide on the manufacturing processes to be used. (See also Figure 95)

The application of form synthesis methods

Having studied the basis of form synthesis methods, it is now possible to look at their applications. The methods for varying the structure, functional surfaces and form may all be applied in very different situations, for instance, (as already mentioned) in deciding on both the total form and the details of product. The methods also may be used for compound products (machines, apparatus, etc) and for products consisting of only one element (bottle openers, fittings, jugs, etc), except that in this case the structure variation method is excluded.

Of course, in demonstrating these methods it has not been the intention to argue that they must *all* be applied to *all* the elements in a product. This is unrealistic. On the other hand, the methods can give rise to a conscious systematic approach to specially important elements, so that these probably are designed as well as possible. The methods may also be used to great advantage in a situation where one has got stuck in designing a given element.

In the collaboration between the design engineer and the process technician, the idea of functional surfaces can be especially valuable. If, for instance, a form detail is discussed because the form and the manufacturing process might have been better matched, it is easier to alter the form of the connecting material than that of the functional surfaces, because these are adjusted to corresponding surfaces in other elements.

Apart from the above-mentioned occasions for using form variation methods, the latter can also make the basis for an attitude of mind which results in a sharpened awareness of what one is working with in a real situation (structure, functional surfaces, form), and which leads to a greater wealth of ideas through a more or less subconscious form variation.

Making models

Whatever the product, the form design work can be carried out with the help of different kinds of models. For a design engineer the most important kind of models are graphical ones, i.e. sketches and drawings. We have, therefore, so far exclusively used these when describing the form variation methods. Other categories of models, however, are also relevant for the design engineer.

Form models can be used in many different situations in a design project.

The decisive factor is:
  what the model will be used for.
On the basis of this can be decided:
  how detailed the model must be, and
  of what material it must be made.

A conscious decision on the degree of detail and the choice of material is necessary for an optimum model, i.e. one which as cheaply as possibly expresses what is needed. The use to which the model is put to affects the choice of degree of detail and of modelling material and this is illustrated in the examples on pages 90—92.

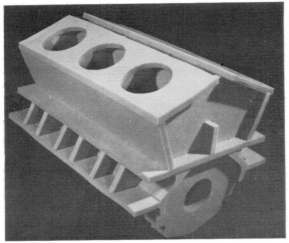

Figure 81   Model of a diesel engine mounting constructed in foam rubber, With rough models such as these it is possible to obtain a first impression of the correlation between rigidity and the different stiffeners

Figure 81 shows some models that have been used for an evaluation of the relative rigidity of differently designed mountings for diesel engines. The models are used in the early design stages when it has to be decided where in space the material must be concentrated (in the form of ribs). Relatively rough models of foam rubbers are therefore suitable, partly because they are quick and cheap to make, and partly because the degree of rigidity can be assessed by slight finger pressure, as the bulging can be seen.

Figure 82 shows a model of the tea maker discussed in Chapter 1. The model has only been used to assess the conditions during use and it is, therefore, very roughly constructed in plastic foam. The model was not to be used for judging the appearance, as it would then have had to be more detailed and so become too expensive. The appearance was judged on the background of another type of model, namely, three-dimensional sketches.

Figure 82   Model of a teamaker in plastic foam. This model can be used to evaluate the conditions during use

Figures 83 and 84 show two models that have both been used to assess operation, space and appearance. Both are made of plastic foam, cardboard and wood. Figure 83 shows a model of the test tube filling machine (Figure 50) previously mentioned, and Figure 84 shows a model of a machine for the automatic labelling of filled test tubes.

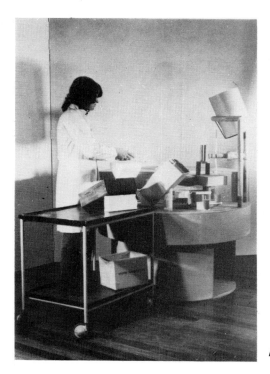

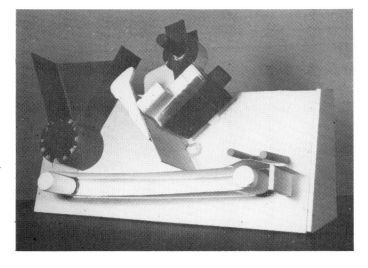

Figure 83   Model of test tube filling machine (see Figure 50). The materials used are plastic foam, cardboard and wood. The model is used for evaluation of conditions during use. (Courtesy of The Institute for Product Development, Technical University of Denmark)

Figure 84   Model of a machine for the automatic labelling of filled test tubes. It is made of plastic foam and cardboard and used for an evaluation of conditions during use as well as appearance. (This was a student project from the Laboratory of Engineering Design, University of Denmark)

The model in Figure 85 has been used to evaluate the basic form of a coin-operated telephone; it is made of clay. Figure 86 shows a model of the finished telephone. The latter has been used to demonstrate the instrument to potential customers before it was in production. It is made of plaster of paris and is so detailed as to be indistinguishable from the real telephone.

Figure 85   Model of a pay telephone made in clay. It is used to evaluate the basic shape of the telephone. (See also Figure 86). (The model was made by Henning Andreasen for GNT Automatic Ltd)

Figure 86   Model of pay telephone made in plaster of paris. It is so detailed as to be indistinguishable from the finished telephone. (This model was also made by Henning Andreasen)

3 FORM FACTORS

3. Form Factors

3.1 The origination of form requirements

The great multiplicity of form design possibilities that may be drawn up in a specfic situation — either by such methods as were described in the previous chapter or simply by intuition — may frighten the unprepared. The question quickly arises of how to reject the unsuitable solutions. It was seen earlier how the product synthesis may be characterised by a continuous alternation between searching for and selecting ideas, and it was mentioned that one ought only to select if suitable criteria for selection are present.

The criteria used are formulated by the designer on the basis of requirements from the outside world. As all the stages in the life of the product (Figure 4) can give rise to demands and requirements in respect of the product we can get a general idea of where these originate. The situation may be described as a force field where a number of forces try to pull the product in different directions. The final product will then represent an equilibrium — a compromise — where the forces balanced each other. Figure 87 illustrates these conditions. On the outside are a number of requirements, product factors, stemming from the life of the product, which influence it through the criteria that are formulated. In the middle are the five basic properties — structure, form, material, dimension and surface — which specify the product. These properties are specified in the product synthesis in such a way that the criteria are fulfilled as far as possible. From the basic properties are derived all other properties of the product, particularly the function, which is the central property in the process of use.

If we consider the basic property of form in particular, we find that the influences arise, on the one hand, from the product factors mentioned above, and, on the other hand, from the other basic properties, as these are not independant variables.

The dependence of the form on the other basic properties will be discussed in the following section. The remainder of the chapter deals with the dependence of form on the product factors, which in this connection are called form factors. The following paragraphs are only intended to hint at the influence of the separate form factors in order to demonstrate the interplay. A more profound study of certain of the factors, e.g. 'technologically correct' design, can be found in other literature.

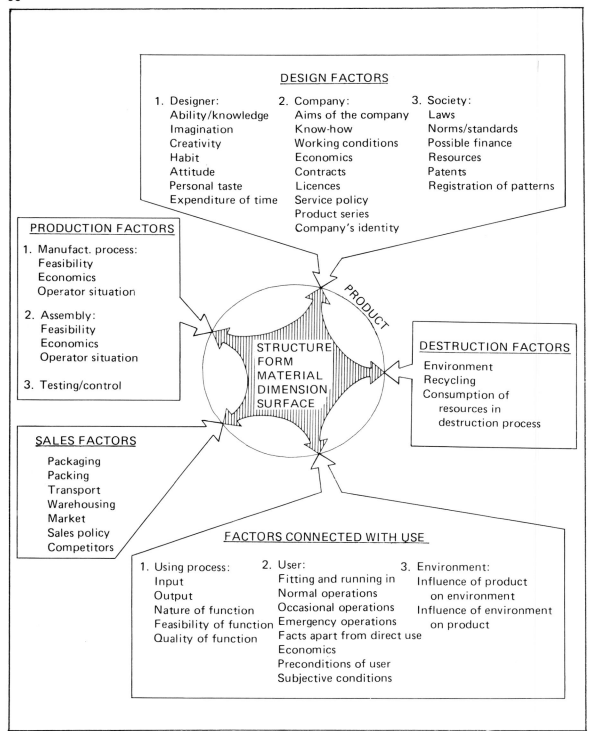

Figure 87   Survey of the life of the product

3.2 The interdependence of the basic properties

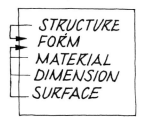

The fact that the basic properties are not independent can be seen in practice by the impossibility of deciding on them separately. The structure cannot be finally chosen until the consequences to the form have been estimated, and the form cannot be determined until material, dimensions and surface have been considered. It is therefore very important to recognize the interplay between the basic properties and the form.

The influence of the structure on the form is direct, as already mentioned (sections 2.1 and 2.2) and illustrated in Figure 88. The dependence of the form on the material, dimension and surface is a little more difficult to identify, because it takes place indirectly.

The interaction of the material and form occurs in two ways. Firstly, the form depends on the production processes by which the material can be shaped, and so the form depends indirectly on the material. Secondly, the properties of the material play a major role in determining the form e.g. the strength, elasticity and weight of the material (see Figure 89).

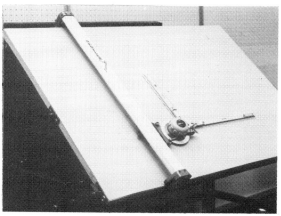

Figure 88   Two drawing instruments with different structures. This illustrates the dependence of form on structure

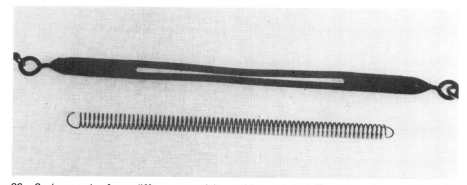

Figure 89   Springs made of two different materials — rubber and steel. The different properties of the materials result in very different form designs

The influence of the dimensions on the form is illustrated in Figure 90. What counts here is the fact that, with the change of size of the object, the practicable production processes alter. The criteria, e.g. the price of the material and the weight, also change. The influence of the surface on the form takes place indirectly through the choice of production process.

Figure 90   Cog-wheels showing the influence of the dimensions (size) on the form

Figure 91   The separate products in a product series are usually so designed that they have the greatest possible number of common form features (Danfos Ltd.)

3.3 Design factors

The designer

The designer has a decisive influence on the form of the product, as he is the one who must both produce the ideas and choose the design. The designer affects the form partly through ability, knowledge and imagination — as far as seeking solutions is concerned. Choice is influenced by the designer's personal taste, attitude and habits. Even when the stipulations for the form design are binding, there is always some freedom for the imagination of the designer to come into play.

The company

Among the many product factors that stem from the company the following may be mentioned — company objectives, know-how, working conditions, economics, contracts, licences, service policy, etc. None of these have a direct influence on the form.

All the same, it will often be the case that the form of a greater or lesser portion of the products have a common character. This fact is most clearly seen in product series, i.e. groups of products with the same of related functions. An example is shown in Figure 91.

Figure 92   A group of products with common form features can help to make up the identity of a company (Bang and Olufsen)

Sometimes a firm tries consciously to maintain a certain identity. The aim of such a company identity is to create faith in the company, as well as to mark its products as against other comparable products, so that the user experiences the company and its products in the same way each time.

This — together with the fact that the user in many cases uses several connected or related products from the same company — leads to the expediency of aiming at common features in appearance. Such a 'house style' may be based on common form traits as well as characteristic choice of materials and surfaces.

The society

There are two aspects of the society in which the product will be used, that must be taken into account in the form design (and, of course, also early on in the creation of the product). These are firstly, consideration of the members of the society, and secondly, conforming to its norms and laws. Among the members of society to be considered first is the user, a fact which will be discussed later in this chapter. There are also all the people who come into contact with the product. These may be people who have to listen to their neighbour's motor lawn mower, to an aeroplane or a speedboat, and all those who each day have to look at other people's cars, excavators and cranes, buses, trains, etc.

Norms and standards exist in areas where safety factors are decisive, or where frequent use makes standardisation necessary, for example: nuts and bolts, washers, fish boxes, railway carriages, and containers.

Pattern registration is a legal protection, which says that other people have no right to simply copy an originally designed product. The law on patterns says among other things:

A pattern means in this law the model for the appearance of an article or for an ornament.
The person who has produced a prototype, or to whom the person's right has been transferred, may in accordance with this law by registration acquire a monopoly for commercial exploitation of the design.
The pattern will only be registered if its is essentially different from what was known before the date of application.

In designing a product, patent registration may come into the picture in two ways — partly as limitations of the design possibilities, if registered products of a similar nature exist in the market, and partly as a protection for one's own product. Figure 93 shows an example of a registered product.

Patents may also play a part as conditions in designing a product, so that certain form possibilities must be left out, if they are described in an existing patent. Normally, patents concern principles and structures.

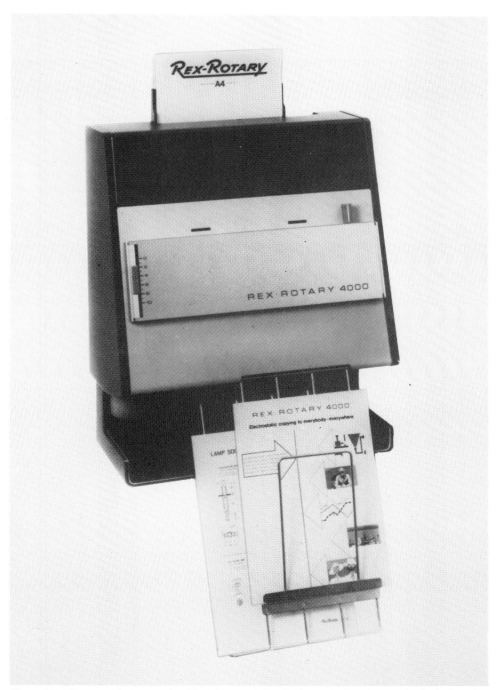

Figure 93 A patented photocopier. The characteristic of this particular photocopier is the fact that the original is put in from above and the copy is produced vertically (Zeuthen and Aagaard Ltd.)

3.4 Production factors

One of the most important questions to be faced when designing a product is how the production will be carried out. Production can be divided into the manufacture of the parts, the assembly and the testing and control. The manufacturing and the assembly processes are very closely linked to the form of the parts.

In section 2.3 on form variation, the different examples did not end with detailed design suggestions, but with a series of form concepts. There is a natural reason for this, namely that a product or a part cannot be designed in detail until one has chosen the material, manufacturing process and assembly process.

The stages in the design of an element are shown in Figure 94, starting from considerations of functional surfaces over two form concept levels to the choice of processes and a final design of details. The loop round the choice of processes means that, at any point, it is possible to split the element into several part elements which are later assembled. Correspondingly, it is sometimes possible to integrate several elements into one. The stage of form division/form integration must thus be thought of as a last level of ideas, which may be used if one cannot easily produce and assemble one's elements.

Figure 95 shows different detailed designs for a pulley (see also Figures 77 to 80). From these diagrams it can be seen that there is a close relationship between elements, the manufacturing and the assembly processes.

Figure 96 shows two bearings where the housing of one bearing is made in one piece (cast) and, the second is made of pressed sheet in two parts that are subsequently assembled. Figure 97 shows two versions of a frame for an electricity meter. Here again one version is made in one piece (pressure die cast), while the other one is made of stamped out parts that are assembled by spot-welding. In both cases there are differences in choice of material, form division, manufacturing and assembly processes.

If we return to the model of the form design stages in Figure 94 it must be appropriate to give an example of how the synthesis may look in the last stages. In Figure 98 we have taken as a starting point the earlier mentioned fork joint (see Figures 59 to 60). The form concept on which the detailed design proposals are built is shown top left, and it is assumed that the joint is approx. 100 mm long and that the material is steel. We first examine by which processes or combinations of processes the fork joint can be manufactured as one element. Next, we

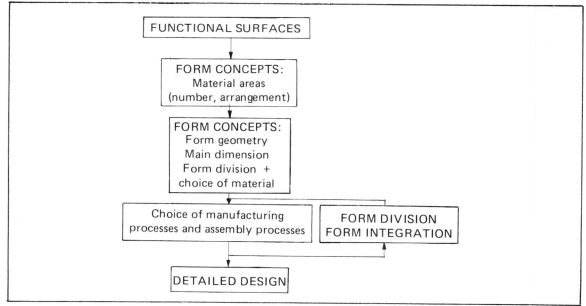

Figure 94   The form design stages in a design project. The stages are gone through for each element

ALTERNATIVE FORM DESIGNS

Different technological processes

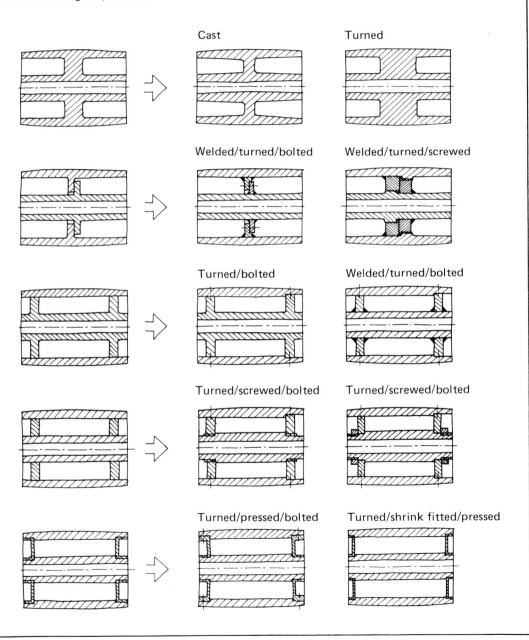

Cast

Turned

Welded/turned/bolted

Welded/turned/screwed

Turned/bolted

Welded/turned/bolted

Turned/screwed/bolted

Turned/screwed/bolted

Turned/pressed/bolted

Turned/shrink fitted/pressed

Figure 95   Different detailed designs for a pulley. (See also Figures 77 to 80)

suggest four new form concepts by form division, and finally each of these is examined for possibilities for manufacturing the elements and for the assembly process.

Altogether the example gives fourteen practical ways in which the joint can be produced. Obviously not all are equally suitable in a specific situation. The choice depends on such factors as the number to be produced, the tolerance required, surface requirements and many other factors. These requirements will be dealt with more thoroughly in the following section.

Figure 96   Two bearings where the casings are respectively cast and made from pressed sheets assembled with bolts (Courtesy SKF)

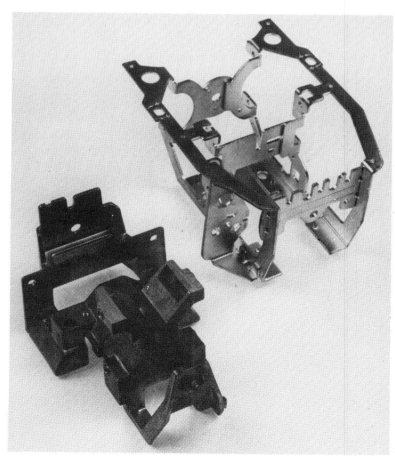

Figure 97   Two frames for an electricity meter. One frame is pressure die cast and the other is punched out, bent and spot-welded

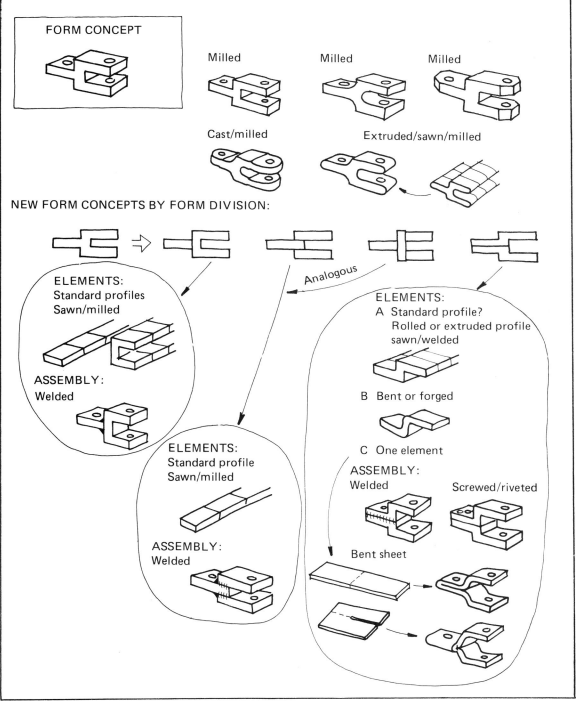

Figure 98   Examples of interplay between form concept, form division and choice of manufacturing and assembly processes. (See also Figures 59 and 60)

The manufacturing process

A condition for being able to choose an optimum manufacturing process is that the best possible agreement can be achieved between the design and the process requirements. This means that the order shown in Figure 94 — form concept, choice of manufacturing and assembly processes, design of details — must be understood, bearing in mind that first the form concepts are drawn up, then the process possibilities are examined, and finally the form concept and the processes are chosen as far as possibly simultaneously. It is thus usually not enough to adjust the detailed form to the process, if an optimum product is to emerge.

The problem of choosing the manufacturing process before the design of the details has been taken too far often occurs in discussions between the designer and the process technician. The former often tends to forget the manufacturing process so that the latter has no possibility of optimising his contribution. The ideal would be if the process technician could come into the picture early so that he could take part in assessing the form concepts at the first stage. In a possible discussion of proposals for alterations based on the manufacturing process, the idea of functional surfaces is valuable. A functional surface can only be altered if other alterations are made simultaneously elsewhere in the system, while an alteration of the areas between the functional surfaces can be made with much greater freedom.

As a rule the designer must have an intimate knowledge of the manufacturing processes available. The fact that (in the bigger firms) there may be process technicians who can assist in the detailed design does not excuse the designer from knowing intimately the existing processes. The designer must know about the form geometries that can be created with a given process, including the tools and fixings. He must also know what materials can be used in the process and the tolerances which can be achieved and the surface finish. Using this information as a background the designer must be able to design his object so that it is cheap to manufacture.

How in practice is it possible to choose the best possible form concept and manufacturing process? Obviously this can only be done from a number of criteria which may be divided into the following categories: feasibility, economics and operator situation.

The manufacturing process: feasibility

The factors concerning feasibility in connection with the choice of process are as follows:
form geometry,
material,
size/dimensions,
surface requirements,
tolerance requirements,
form (availability) of the input materials.

The first three factors decide whether a given process is at all possible. Each process has its own characteristics and limitations, as shown in Figure 99. When initially considering various processes one should not choose those at the extremes, so that the size is theorectically possible but in practice difficult to achieve.

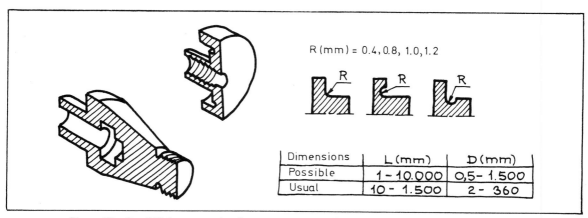

R (mm) = 0.4, 0.8, 1.0, 1.2

Dimensions	L (mm)	D (mm)
Possible	1 - 10.000	0,5 - 1.500
Usual	10 - 1.500	2 - 360

Figure 99   Possibilities concerning form geometry and dimensions that can be realised by turning

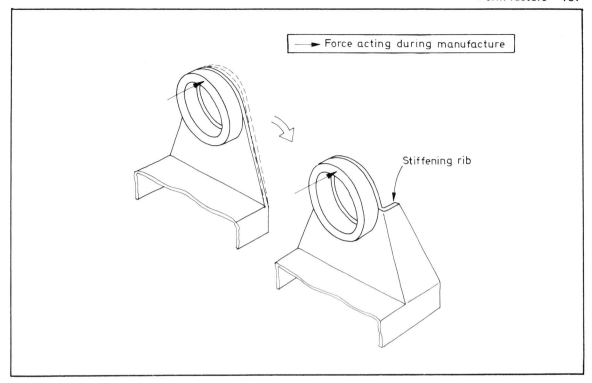

Figure 100   Bearings bracket where the forces acting on it during manufacture have been taken into consideration, so that the tolerances can be maintained

The factors of surface and tolerance requirements must also be included when choosing the process. It is not enough that these requirements can theoretically be met, but they must also apply to the specific object. The example in Figure 100 shows a bearing bracket, the design of which is suited to the forces that act on it during production. The only purpose the stiffening rib serves, in this case, is to restrict the flexibility during the production sufficiently for the desired tolerances to be achieved.

The last factor mentioned in the list is the form of the materials used. It is necessary that the required materials exist or can be obtained in the desired form.

The manufacturing process: economics involved in the choice of process

Economic factors in connection with the choice of process are:

the number of processes required,
materials: supply, price, quantity or own manufacture;
quantities to be produced;
machinery;
investment in new machinery;
special tools.

An object may be produced directly in one process, if one is lucky, or in several successive processes.

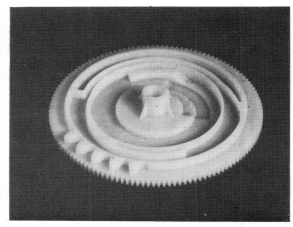

Figure 101   Two versions of control wheels in a photocopier. In the prototype the wheel is turned and milled (left), while in the final version it is die-cast (right). (Courtesy of Zeuthen & Aagaard Ltd.)

The economics of the manufacture depend on which and how many processes must be gone through before the object is finished. One must also consider the necessary transport, handling and 'fixings' between the separate processes.

The availability of the desired materials must be examined. It should be decided whether they can be bought in the required form, and under what conditions, or whether the company itself must produce them.

The quantity in which the object is to be produced is decisive when deciding which manufacturing processes will be economic. Processes that require big investments in tools and machinery (e.g. die casting and drop forging) can only be considered where large numbers of objects are involved, while those processes that are immediately available (e.g. turning, milling and welding) are well suited to the production of single objects or series of objects. Figure 101 shows an example of this.

As already mentioned, the last three factors —

machinery, investment in new machinery and special tools — are closely connected with the quantities to be produced.

The manufacturing process: the operator

At the same time as an object is designed and a process decided on, a job for an operator is laid down. This must be done as a conscious effort, where the operator's situation is used to influence the form design and the choice of process. One must ensure that the operator can carry out the process appropriately without unnecessary work load and risk and, for instance, without unnecessary demands for precision or speed.

But even if in principle the operator's conditions may be allowed for, there is still a decisive factor remaining. Has the company the necessary know-how, can others be trained, or must new workers be employed?

The manufacturing process: the economics of the detailed design

After the form concept and the manufacturing process are chosen according to the criteria of feasibility, economics and operator situation there is still the detailed design to be decided (see Figure 94). The last task is to design the details in such a way that the object can be manufactured in the most suitable way by the chosen process, and that the desired function may be sufficiently well realised.

Form design guidelines for all the usual processes can be found in the specialist literature, and therefore the characteristics of the various processes will not be discussed here. A few general guidelines can,

however, be laid down with a view to as economic a form design as possible. They are:

number and nature of 'fixings',
number and nature of tools,
number and extent of processes,
accessibility for tools,
consumption of materials.

These guidelines are illustrated in Figure 102 to 106. Figure 107 shows a complete example in which many of the economically important factors are mentioned.

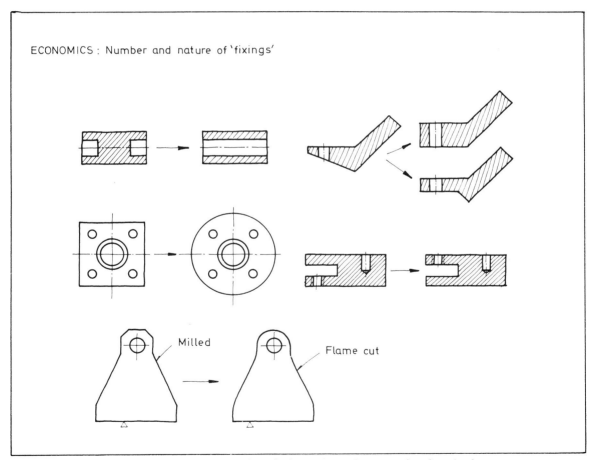

Figure 102   Form designs that take into account the economics of production

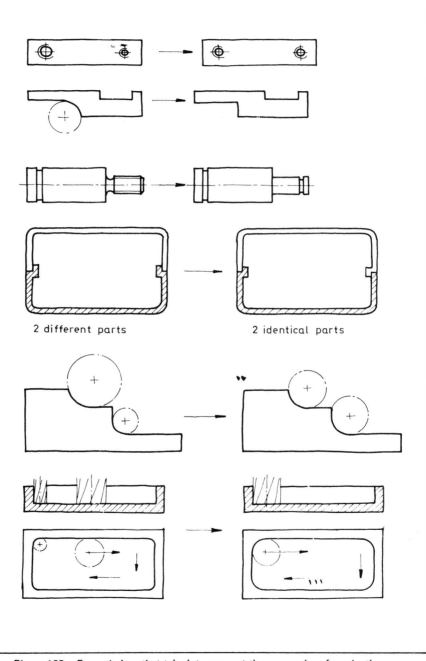

ECONOMICS : Number and nature of tools

2 different parts   2 identical parts

Figure 103   Form designs that take into account the economics of production

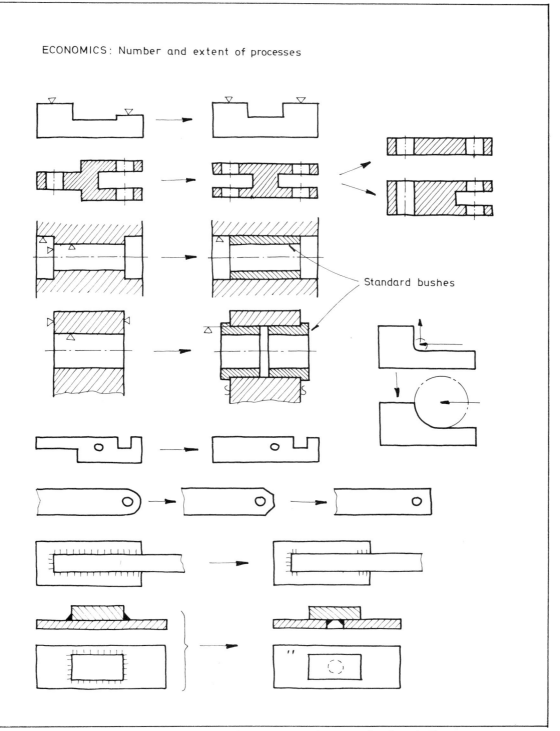

Standard bushes

Figure 104   Form designs that take into account the economics of production

112

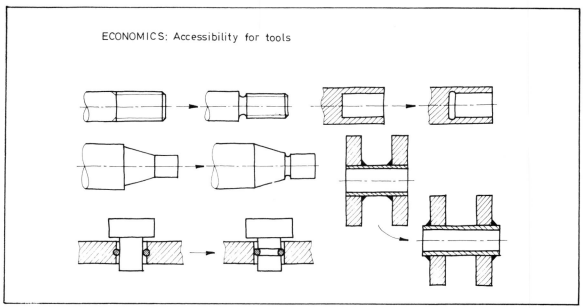

ECONOMICS: Accessibility for tools

Figure 105   Form designs that take into account the economics of production

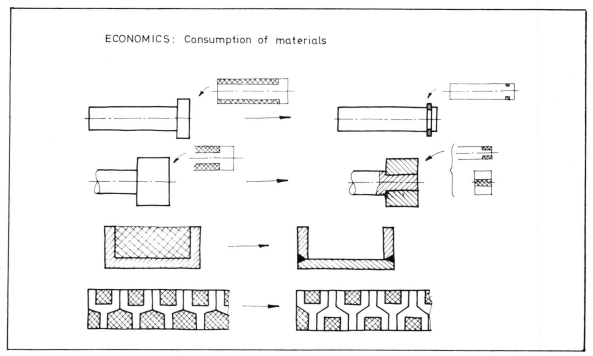

Figure 106   Form designs that take into account the economics of production

5 000 pieces a year

starting material:	020 brass rod
manufacture:	turning thread cutting milling
consumpt. of material:	object 25 gr. shavings 70 gr.
investment:	nil
production cost:	50p

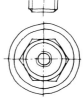

50 000 pieces a year

starting material:	020 brass rod
manufacture:	hot pressing turning thread cutting
Consumption of mat:	object 25 gr. shavings 25 gr.
investment:	£900
production cost:	35p

200 000 pieces a year

starting material:	12 mm hexagonal brass rod 1.5 mm brass strip
manufacture:	turning thread cutting punching assembly
consumption of material:	object 20 gr + 3 gr shavings 20 gr cut 2 gr
investment:	£3600
production cost:	25p

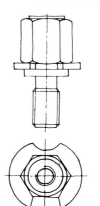

Figure 107   Three versions of a thread spindle corresponding to different product quantities. The most important economic factors are listed

Assembly

The close connection between the assembly process and the manufacturing processes was mentioned on page 105 and is illustrated in the following examples. The assessments that must be made before choosing an assembly process are (as in the case of the manufacturing process) feasibility, economics and situation of the operator, and the factors are completely parallel to the factors in choosing the manufacturing process (see pages 110—112). Figure 108 shows examples from a photocopier where the prototype and the final machine are compared. The illustration shows, above, an example of the way in which the number of operations in fitting a mirror can be reduced if one goes to the expense of a die cast tool.

The lower illustration shows an example of how a traditional way of fitting a pin can be simplified if the assembly process is carefully thought out.

After the assembly process has been chosen (and the manufacturing ones as well) the product details must be designed in such a way that an optimum assembly can be achieved. As a check the following list of general sub-operations in assembly may be used:

recognise   line up
grasp   fit in
move to contact area   move along contact area
orientate   secure

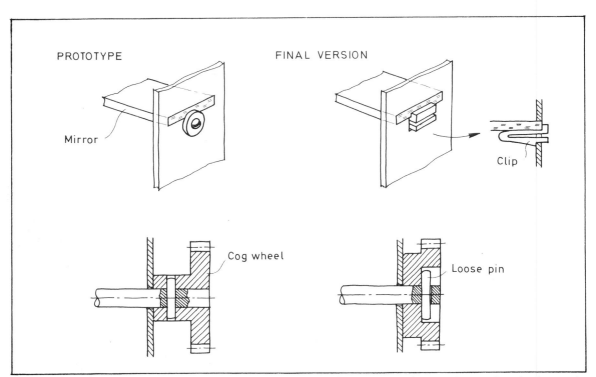

Figure 108 Comparison between form design details in a prototype (function model) and the final version of a photocopier. Above, fixing a mirror to a frame; below, fixing a cog wheel on an axle (Courtesy Zeuthen & Aagaard Ltd.)

Figure 109 shows examples of the way in which some sub-operations can be made easier by the form design. These considerations apply whether the assembly is manual or automatic. Figure 110 shows the assembly of a stop button in an electric switch. On the button is printed the word STOP, and in order to ensure that it is put on the right way up, the bottom is designed with a groove that corresponds to a knob on the edge of the hole.

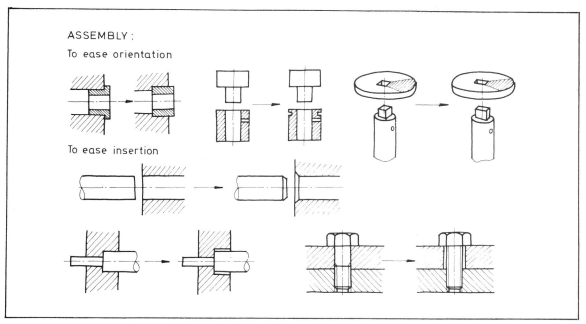

Figure 109   Form design details that illustrate how the assembly is taken into account

Figure 110   Form design details that ensure a stop button is fitted in the correct position (Danfoss Ltd.)

3.5 Sales and distribution factors

Factors that influence distribution and sales constitute a large and mixed group made up partly of the physical conditions such as packaging, packing, transport and warehousing, partly of market conditions and partly of the sales situation of the company.

Transport considerations mean that one must think about possible results of shocks and shaking. Delicate parts may have to be secured; damp, dirt, corroding fumes, etc must also be considered. If the weight of the product can cause problems it may be necessary to divide big heavy parts into smaller elements. One must also check on whether the dimensions of the product are too great for it to be economically transported and on whether, for instance, it can pass through a door.

An example of the way in which a suitable form design can make for convenient transport may be illustrated by the lawn mower in Figure 111. By far the biggest part of such a lawn mower is the handle, which if made in one piece would take up a disproportionate amount of space. This was, indeed, the case in many early models. A solution to this problem may be seen in the illustration, as the handle is divided in two places, so that it can be packed without taking up more room than the cutting unit.

Figure 111   Lawn mower where the handle is divided in two places solely for reasons of packaging and transport (Courtesy of Ginge Fabrikker Ltd.)

Matters to be taken into account in warehousing may, for instance, be reducing the space occupied, minimising the sentitivity of the product to damp and dirt etc, and to ensure that several objects of the same sort can be stacked. Figure 112 shows how storing conditions can influence the design of plastic buckets. There are here two problems in connection with storage, on the one hand the objects must take up as little space as possible (i.e. they must be stackable), and on the other hand, they must be easy to separate. Alteration of the angle gives more compact stacking. Squashing in the stack can be prevented by a vertical rib.

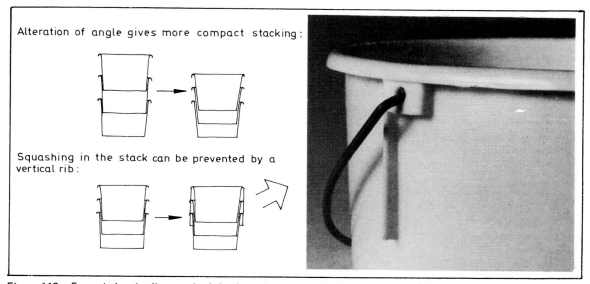

Alteration of angle gives more compact stacking:

Squashing in the stack can be prevented by a vertical rib:

Figure 112   Form design details on a plastic bucket, where storage is taken into account (Courtesy Superfos Emballage Ltd.)

3.6 Factors concerning the product in use

Process evaluation: Input, output and function

When a product is being used the user of the product achieves a desired process (see also page 6). Such a process may, for instance, be the drilling of holes (electric drill), the mincing of meat (meat mincer), the moving of water (pump) and the moving of food (fork). This is the function of the product (the main function, see also page 9); one can think of the usage and the function as two sides of the same coin; the usage may be described by the object that alters a condition, while the function describes the simultaneous operation of the product (or tool). We thus get product factors from both the object — in the starting state these are called input and in the final state output — and from this function.

If we first examine the influence of input and output of the form design of a product we must remember that the areas where it is in contact with its surroundings are the external functional surfaces (see page 48). It is on these surfaces that input and output have their greatest influence. Countless examples of such an influence may be mentioned, for example, nuts that affect the form of an open-ended or a box spanner, a punching tool that transfers its form to the object, etc. Figure 113 shows a number of irons from different periods. Here the shape of the functional surface against the material has been preserved almost unaltered through the ages. This shape has two characteristics, first that it constitutes a flat, smooth surface area against the material, in order that this may itself be made smooth, and secondly that it is pointed so that the material is spread out before it is pressed smooth.

Next, let us look at the influence of function on the form. Functions can be found at many levels in a product and the main function may thus affect the total form of the product and the sub-functions the form of the elements. The influence of the functions is, however, very dependent on the intended functions. In certain cases there is an unambigous connection between function and form, as for instance in the cam and the mirror in Figure 114 (top).

In other cases a certain connection exists, even though there is some freedom. The propeller and the thread are examples of this. Finally there are situations where there is no connection between the function and the form, as for instance, the case round a meter or a computer.

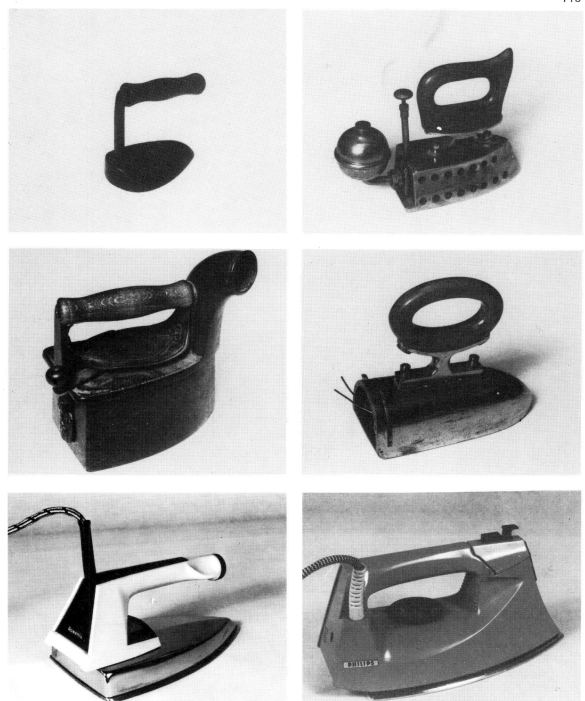

Figure 113   Irons from different periods. The functional surface which rubs against the material in all these designs is unchanged. (The two lower illustrations are by courtesy of Rowenta and Philips)

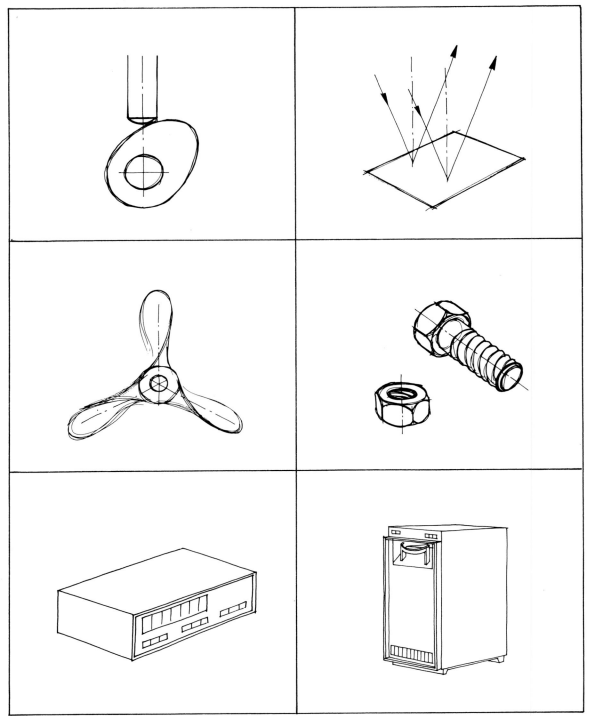

Figure 114   Interaction between function and form. Above, absolute connection; centre, a certain degree of connection; below, no connection

Process realisation: Realisation of the function

It is obvious that to merely state there is a more or less close connection between function and form, as described previously, is not particularly constructive, but a description of the factors that come into play may illuminate important problems for the designer. The functional factors may be divided into two categories:
    realisation
    quality of function.

The former may involve such factors as:
    function interval (can the function be realised in the desired size?)
    quality of the output
    exactness (precision)
    capacity
    speed of the process
    effectiveness.
    Examples of the dependence of some of these factors on the form of the functional surfaces are shown in Figure 115.

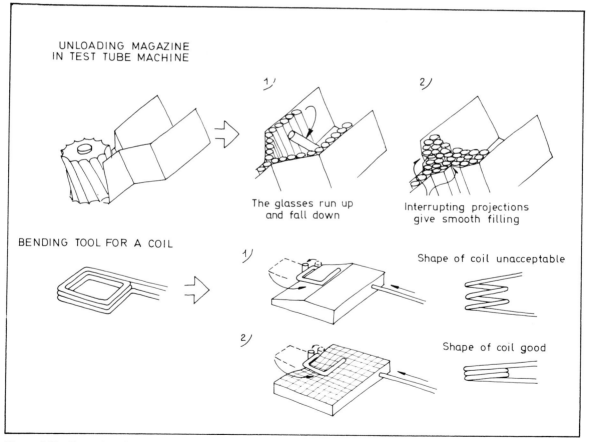

Figure 115   Examples of the way in which the feasability of a desired function is tied in with the form design of a functional surface. Above, an unloading magazine in a test tube machine (see also Figure 53); below, a bending tool for a coil of thick copper wire

Process realisation: Quality of the function

When it has been decided that a given function is possible, the next stage is to establish under what conditions this will be done and the extent to which the desired function can be achieved. The functional factors at this stage may be called quality of function factors, for example:

    is the function reproducible
    parameter sensitivity
    reliability
    safety
    stability.

These factors can be taken into account by choosing and building-in suitable qualities such as:

    strength
    rigidity
    hardness
    elasticity, etc.

Figure 116 shows examples of form designs that take the above-mentioned quality of function factors into consideration.

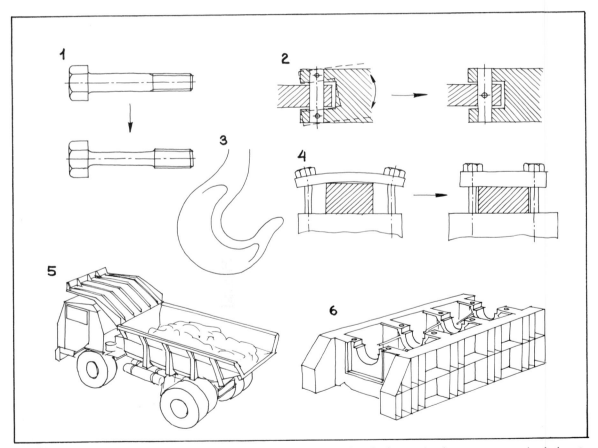

Figure 116   1. A bolt where deeper bends reduce the slot sensitivity. 2. Connection between two mechanical parts, where the assembly is most rigid if the axle journal is attached by a pin through the middle. 3 and 4. Form designs that give strength. 5 and 6. Form designs that provide rigidity (a truck body and supporting frame for a diesel engineer)

User or operator: A survey of the factors

The user naturally demands certain things of the product. One of the most fundamental of these is that the product must be simple to use, i.e. that its use must be easy and uncomplicated with the least possible mental and physical effort.

In order to take adequate account of such requirements the designer must acquire — or at least be able to find — information on the dimensions, senses, perception, muscular performance, tiredness, etc of the human body. If there are special categories of users, such as handicapped people, children, etc, special attention must be given to this information. It is then the designers job to utilise this knowledge together with a general appreciation of the interplay between 'man and the machine' (which is covered in ergonomics), so that the product is designed as suitably as possible. If a designer overlooks this very important background knowledge the result is often a product that may be either difficult to use, or gives a bad working posture (and restulging in back trouble), or that may hold risks of wrong operation, etc. An example is shown in Figure Figure 117. Here the design of the lathe is such that an operator with normal body dimensions cannot avoid an unreasonable posture, which puts a great strain on his back.

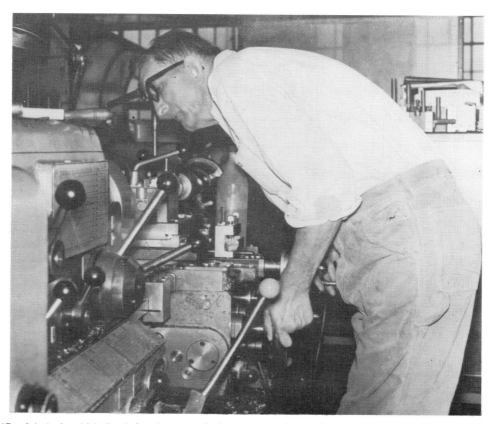

Figure 117   A lathe in which the design does not take into account the requirement of a good working posture

Figure 118 shows an example of a product where the design takes the greatest possible account of the user's situation. The noise meter is built so that at the top there is a directional microphone which picks up and records the noise coming in. The top part of the instrument almost a bottleneck to avoid reflecting surfaces that may have an effect on the exactitude of the microphone.

The noise meter is also designed so that it is comfortable to hold when metering. Handling is taken into consideration by a suitable arrangement of such elements as control knobs, dials, etc. These are designed in such a way that they are easily accessible when the instrument is directed to a given noise source.

The interaction between man and the machine will now be studied more closely. We can think of a machine and an operator as a system that can act on the surroundings in a desired way, i.e. to make use of the product. Figure 119 shows such a man/machine system, where the interplay between the machine and the operator and between them and the surroundings is shown.

The interaction between the machine and the operator may be divided into four categories, involving a number of factors:

handling conditions in connection with installation and running in.

normal operation, e.g. nature of job, good working posture, safety, easy movements and accessibility.

occasional operation, e.g. cleaning, maintenance, adjustments and repairs.

emergency operation, e.g. emergency stop and fire.

Apart from these four categories which concern the operation of the machine under various circumstances there are four additional categories, that have no direct connection with the operation. They are:

circumstances outside direct operation, e.g. installation, mobility, storage space,

economics, e.g. initial cost, running costs, depreciation,

user requirements, e.g. advance knowledge, instruction, training, education,

subjective circumstances, e.g. psychological circumstances in operating the machine, appearance.

From the above eight categories, the following have a close connection with the form: normal operation, occasional operations and subjective circumstances. These will be further studied in the following section.

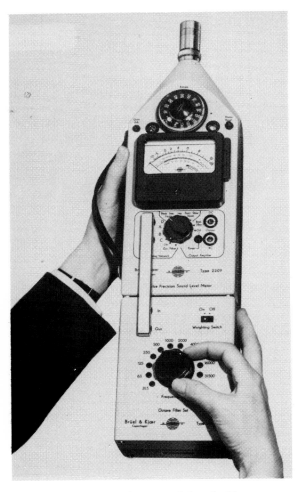

Figure 118   A noise meter designed with consideration of the circumstances under which it will be used

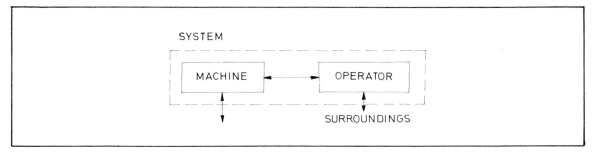

Figure 119   Man/machine system

User or operator: Normal operations

Among the factors which concern the normal operation of the machine must be mentioned:

nature of the job (aim: a meaningful job),
good working posture,
safety,
easy movements,
accessibility,
convenient communication with the machine,
no unpleasant noise, heat, reflections, etc.

The three factors of working posture, movements and accessibility are closely tied in with the design. This is primarily a question of taking account of the human dimensions and performance possibilities, so that one can avoid badly designed products such as the lathe in Figure 117. There are a number of books on ergonomics and anthropometry (i.e. the study of the measurements of the human body) which cover this subject.

Communication between the operator and the machine involves many design aspects that are worthy of further examination. Without suitable communication the product cannot be used as desired. When information is conveyed from one place to another there is always the risk of error. This can happen in two ways, as shown in Figure 120. On

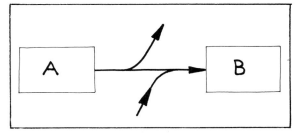

Figure 120   The two possibilities for errors in transferring information from A to B

the one hand information may be lost, or wrong information may be added. The following pages outline a number of circumstances that can contribute to clear an unambigous communication between the operator and the machine.

Let us take as our starting point the man/machine system in Figure 119. A more detailed model is shown in Figure 121. The operator can, in principle, be thought of as comprising three sub-systems, namely the sensory apparatus (eyes, ears, etc.), the decision apparatus (the brain), and motor apparatus (hands, arms and legs). The machine may be divided in the same way into three sub-systems; the process system, the supervision system and the operating system.

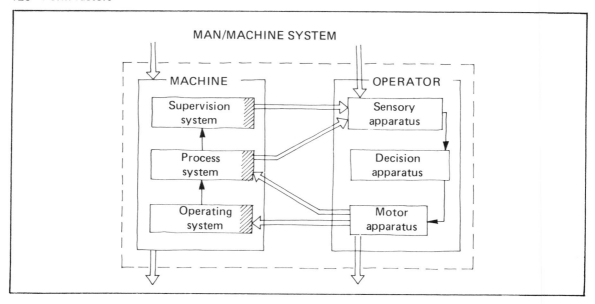

Figure 121   The most important elements and relationships in a man/machine system

Those parts of the machine which are in direct communication with the operator (the hatched areas in the figure) are known as the supervisions area, the operating area and the open process area. The mutual influence between the sub-systems is demonstrated in the illustration. The three areas are symbolically illustrated in Figure 122. Supervision areas and operating areas are often placed together in a control area, while the open process area is kept apart from these. Examples of the arrangement of the areas are shown in Figure 123 and 124.

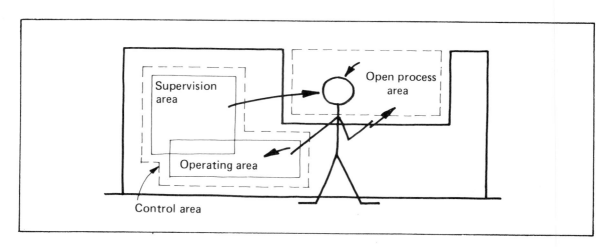

Figure 122   The three areas of a machine with which the operator is in contact

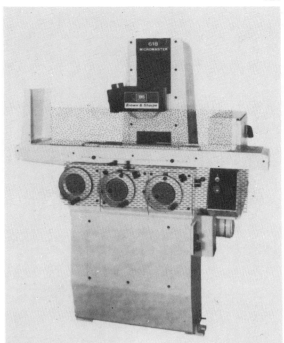

Figure 123 Control area and open process area in a grinding machine and a hydraulic press

Figure 124 Control area and open process area in a copying camera and an electric cooker (Courtesy of Eskofot Ltd. and S.A.G. Ltd)

On a machine, the control areas and the open process area should be arranged in such a way that they are clearly separated. This is helpful to the operator and furthers communication between him and the machine. Sometimes the control area is placed in a separate unit which is physically apart from the machine. This may either be due to a natural functional separation, as e.g. in numerically controlled machine tools, where the control unit is separate from the rest, or it may also be because specific advantages in use may be gained. The latter may be quicker and more convenient handling, the possibility of remote control, greater safety for the operator or perhaps only greater flexibility all round. An example is shown in Figure 125.

On the other hand, if the control area is placed in or on the machine it may be emphasised in various ways. An important factor in this connection is the so-called 'figure on ground effect', which is a fundamental effect in any visual perception. The 'figure on ground effect' tells us that when we look we always notice objects or figures, which thereby become significant, while the background dwindles and perhaps hardly leaves a trace in our consciousness. If one wants to draw attention to something, it may thus be done by using a figure that stands out clearly against the background. On the basis of these facts one can formulate some requirements for the design of the control area:

The contrast in form, colour and surface (texture) between the figure and the background must be optimised. This does not mean that the contrast must be as great as possible (black/white, red/green etc.) as this may make everything seem to flicker. On the contrary, it means that the contrast must be adapted so that the figure stands our clearly from the background without distracting and tiring the eye.

Dimensions between the individual figure and the remaining figures must be adjusted. There must not be figures that get lost in the crowd.

Good lighting must be assured.

Distracting elements must be minimised. These may be e.g. reflections, after images, powerful sources near and dominating figures very close to.

Figure 126 shows a photocopier where the figure ground effect is utilised to emphasis the control area and make it clear.

The individual elements of a control panel constutute two categories, namely the signalling instruments (the supervision area) and the operating instruments (the operating area). We have previously seen how the machine must be designed in such a way that the control areas stand out as a clear and well defined part of the machine. The following pages outline some principles for arranging the individual components of the control panel with regard to effective communication between the operator and the machine.

Three main points manifest themselves in the layout of a control panel, namely the frequency of use

Figure 125 Electric scales, where the control area is separate from the process area (the tray). (Courtesy of Bizerba)

Figure 126 A photocopier with the control area emphasised (Courtesy Oce-Helioprint Ltd)

and the importance of the separate elements, as well as the clarity of the layout. This means that the most often used elements, and, for instance, an emergency stop are placed centrally. While, generally, it is not difficult to decide which elements belong to the two first-mentioned groups it is a more demanding task to arrange the elements in relation to each other in a manner that is clear and simple to grasp. Here, however, perception psychology may help us, especially the branch called gestalt psychology. The most important factors in this connection are the ideas of group and pattern creation on the basis of closeness and similarity.

On control panels with many similar elements, e.g. lights, switches and handles, it is useful to divide these into smaller groups that are easy to scan. Various means may be used for the grouping, namely either collecting the elements into smaller groups by arranging them closer together, or differentiating them by groups, e.g. each group its own colour. It is also possible, of course to form groups by dividing the area of the control panel into different sections with the aid of lines and colours.

Figure 127 shows schematically a control panel with 50 elements. If these are arranged as in (a), they will form an area of a uniform structure, where it is difficult to identify a given element. In (b) to (e) the

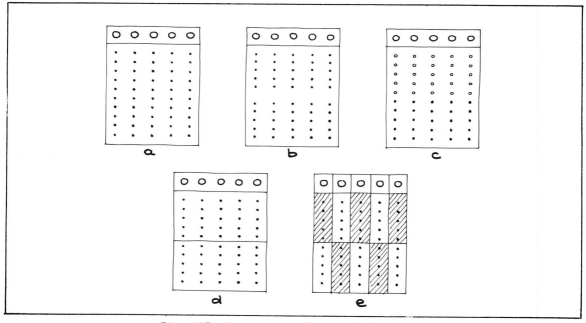

Figure 127   A control panel with many similar elements

Figure 128   Grouping the elements on the background of closeness and similarity (Courtesy IBM)

Figure 129   An element that stands out in an otherwise homogeneous row catches the attention. The picture shows part of a control panel on a computer (Courtesy IBM)

grouping is done respectively by different distance, different colour, division by line and division by coloured areas. These divisions mean that one can quickly — without counting — point to a given element. In other words, by grouping the elements one can ensure much quicker identification of the separate elements that if one had to count to find them. Figure 128 shows yet another example of this.

If, on a control panel, there is a row of similar elements they will be perceived as a homogenous row where no element stands out. One does not notice the separate elements. Now, if one of these is altered, it will at once be clearly distinguishable from the others. This fact may be used in two ways;

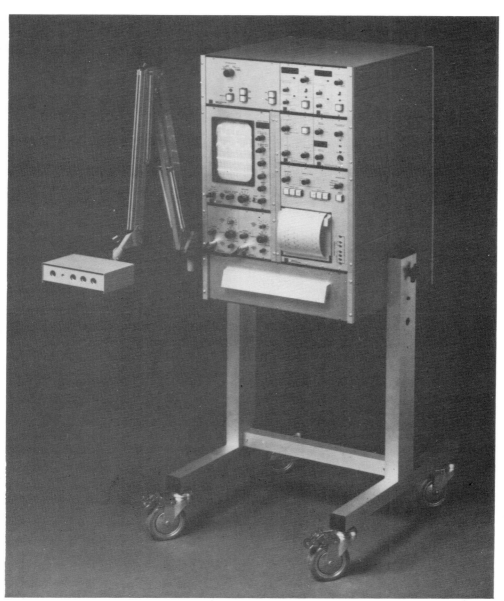

Figure 130   A control panel with groups formed on the basis of proximity, similarity and framed sections (Courtesy DISA Electronic Ltd)

A row of similar elements ought to have the same 'normal' position, i.e. all pointers are vertical and all lights are on during operation, etc. If one of the elements gets out of the normal position it will immediately attract attention, and thus ensure that the alteration is noticed. See Figure 129.

If one of the elements is especially important it can be placed in a row of others that are similar to each other. The one that is different will stand out. As an example may be mentioned a dial with a different shape from the others, or a red emergency stop placed between black control knobs.

Grouping by function is often used as a basis for a control panel layout. The elements that belong together in a functional unit are collected in one group on the panel, either by placing the elements in the individual functional groups closely together (proximity), by making them similar in form or colour (similarity), or by dividing the panel into sections indicated by lines, colours or areas. An example is shown in Figure 130.

An operationally-determined layout of a control panel may be expedient if the elements are used each time in a certain sequence. In this case it will be natural to place the elements in an order corresponding to this sequence, so that by moving one's fingers from one button to the next the sequence is followed correctly (Figure 131).

A process-determined layout of a control panel is

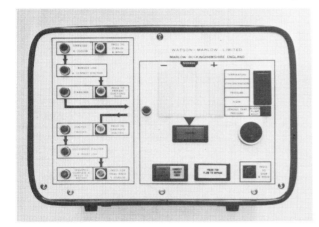

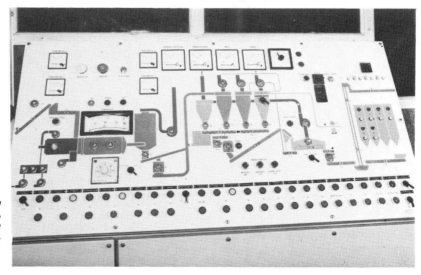

Figure 131 Operationally determined layout of a control panel. The elements of the panel are arranged in the order in which they must be operated (Courtesy Watson-Marlow Ltd)

Figure 132 Process-determined layout of a control panel. The picture shows the control panel of a grass drying plant (Courtesy of Atlas Ltd)

natural if the elements on the panel control a number of components in a process system. The panel may in this case, as shown in Figure 132, be designed as a simplified diagram of the process with the individual elements on the panel so arranged that it is easy to see to which point in the process system they correspond.

User or operator: Occasional operations

Occasional operations are activities in connection with the machine, which do not concern the normal operations, but which are necessary for the continuous use of it. These are:

cleaning,
maintenance,
servicing,
adjusting,
repairs.

How much regard one should pay to these factors depends on both the product and the environment. The designer must remember to consider from which points of view the factors should be taken into account, for instance, whether the product must be easy to clean, or whether it should be designed so that cleaning is unnecessary. Also whether the product must be easy to adjust and repair, or whether it must be built in such a way that parts or subsystems are replaced instead. Easy cleaning is achieved first of all by ensuring easy access and by avoiding slots and holes that can collect dirt (see Figures 133 and 134). The remaining factors are taken into consideration by a design which also gives accessibility, simple assembly/dismantling of components, convenient weight and size of these and safety while performing these jobs.

Figure 133   Meat mincers with suction feet. On the left is a design where meat juices and liquid may run down into the foot which cannot be taken apart. On the right a new design where cleaning has been taken into consideration

Figure 134   Suggested designs for the holder of a dialysis cell (artificial kidney). The equipment is used in a hospital environment, where easy cleaning is an important requirement. The design shown in the lower illustration is therefore preferable

User or operator: Subjective circumstances

Some of the most important and, at the same time, most difficult factors in designing a product concern the user's subjective attitude to it: ·

    psychological facts.
    appearance.

The psychological facts concern the user's reaction to the product; the user may, for instance, feel repulsed/attracted, unsure/confident, oppressed/free while using it (see Figure 190). These factors may be difficult to assess at the design stage, but if one feels that there may be problems, a three-dimensional model may be needed.

From the user's viewpoint the appearance of the product plays an important role. When evaluating the appearance differentiation can be made between the aesthetic element and the influence of style, fashion and habit. The aesthetic side is timeless and universal beauty, while style, fashion and habit depend on time and place.

Figure 135 shows two microscopes from different periods, which both give an aesthetic experience. The particular conditions concerned in aesthetic design will be discussed in greater detail in Chapter 4, which deals exclusively with the appearance of the product.

It is difficult to draw the line between style, fashion and habit. While style is a sort of common denominator for what is current in a certain period with regard to the design of products in industry, applied arts, architecture and art, fashion is short lived and often attached to certain products. Thus the fashion in cars, for instance, has nothing to do with the fashion in the design of domestic appliances. Figures 136 and 137 show examples of style and fashion.

Also, habit must not be overlooked when designing a product. If there is a widespread habitual idea of what the design should be, it can be catastrophic for a company to ignore this. One of the best known

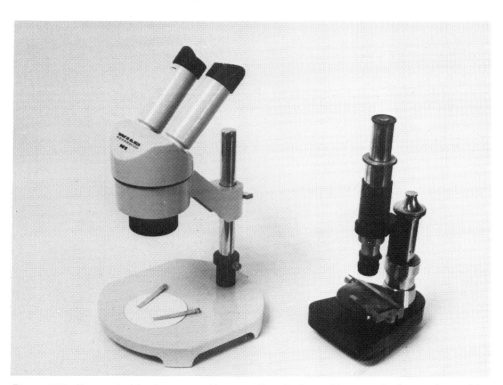

Figure 135   New and old microscopes. However, they both provide an aesthetic experience. (New microscope is by courtesy of Wild Heerbrugg Ltd.)

examples of the force of habit is that of ships, which even today are mostly built with a funnel, though these became unnecessary with the introduction of the diesel engine. Another example is the transistor radio shown in Figure 138 (left). In spite of the fact that it was thoroughly researched both technically and operationally it did not sell, because the form was too remote from the traditional idea which people had of what a transistor radio should look like (Figure 138, right).

Figure 136   The influence of style on form illustrated by telephones and switches (Courtesy of GNT Automatic Ltd, and LK-NES Ltd)

Figure 137 Fashion: Three makes of car having almost identical designs

Environment

The environment in which the product will be used is important for the design in two ways. On the one hand the environment may have to be protected against the effects of the product and, on the other, the product may have to be protected against the effects of the environment.

In cases where a product might possibly damage or perhaps ruin the environment the design must be such that this does not happen. If a product is to be directly operated by a user, one must be aware of the influences to which this person is exposed to and take these into account in the design. If it is a product

Figure 138   Habit. Two transistor radios showing traditional and unusual designs. The design on the right is immediately recognisable as a transistor radio (Courtesy Bang & Olufsen)

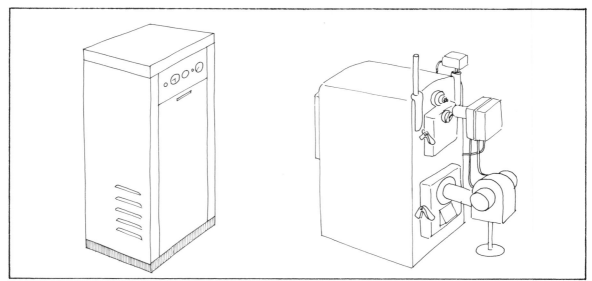

Figure 139   Two oil-fired boilers for different environments, namely a utility room which requires cleanliness and muffling and a cellar without particular requirements

that will be used in a factory one must therefore, through the design, ensure that there is no deterioration of the working environment. Obviously, the same considerations must be shown if people, may have to pass near the product. In the instances mentioned the product may have to be shielded against heat, muffle noise, damp vibrations, etc. An example is shown in Figure 139.

The product is exposed to a number of more or less uncontrolled influences such as high temperatures, corroding liquids and gases, forces, vibrations, etc. Therefore it must be designed so that it can resist these factors adequately.

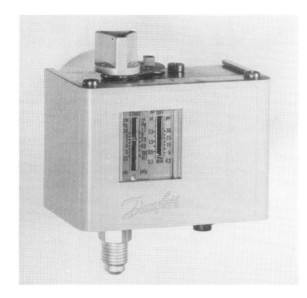

Figure 140   A pressure switch on three different covers to protect it from damp — normal, drip-proof and ray-proof (Courtesy Danfoss Ltd)

The design is influenced by the choice of material and consequently by the choice of manufacturing process. It will also be affected by the possible need for special covering, protective shields, etc. An example is shown in Figure 140, where a pressure switch is designed for three different environments. At the top, is a normal switch for ordinary fairly dry rooms, in the centre a design that is drip proof, i.e. proof against damp and dust, and at the bottom a ray proof type switch i.e. a completely enclosed and very tough version for use in specially exposed locations.

3.7 Destruction factors

The final process that a product goes through during its 'life' (see page 6) is destruction. All products are destroyed either by a gradual breaking down through environmental influences or by destruction by man, i.e. incineration, crushing, melting, cutting up, etc. The destruction factors can be divided into environment considerations, possibilities for recycling and the consumption of resources in the destruction process.

Environmental considerations may be decisive as to whether active destruction is contemplated. If the product, after it has served its purpose constitutes a danger, an eyesore or some other nuisance, it may be designed in such a way that it is easy to dismantle or destroy, or materials may be used which ensure that the natural destruction is speeded up.

Possibilities for recycling material, components or sub-systems ought to be considered in the design. For instance it may be that a tiny alteration in the design makes possible a simple dismantling of a given component or an easy separation of two materials. As the supply of our raw materials becomes shorter it may become more usual to take this factor into account.

The consumption of resources in destruction is mainly a question of using manpower, energy and equipment.

3.8 Evaluation or form design suggestions

Obviously not all the form factors or form criteria previously mentioned can be fully accomodated in a given solution. When evaluating a number of form design suggestions (see Chapter 2 on 'Form synthesis methods') one gets a situation where the different suggestions fulfill the criteria in different ways. The problem may be illustrated by the following example. Which of two suggested solutions is the best one, when one solution is cheap to produce, relatively complicated to operate, expensive to run and of good appearance, while the other solution is dearer to produce, easy to operate, cheap to run and of an unfortunate appearance? The answer must naturally depend on what other criteria should also be taken into account, as well as what weight the individual criteria must be given compared to each other. The evaluation of a number of suggested solutions is therefore a difficult task.

Evaluation may be carried out by a number of more or less formalised techniques. These run from a quite informal evaluation based on intuition to one with several balanced criteria that are weighed separately, after which a complete evaluation is made according to certain rules. The choice of technique for evaluation depends on the level of detailing at which the suggested solutions are formulated. These techniques will not be discussed here as there is a great deal of literature already published on this subject.

Common to all evaluation situations is the fact that the suggested solutions must be modelled (in the widest sense, e.g. in a sketch or in a three-dimensional model, see Chapter 2), so that one can examine the qualities to be evaluated, such as space, operation, appearance, etc. The various suggested solutions which must be evaluated concurrently, must necessarily be modelled with the same degree of detail, so that a solution that might possibly be more thoroughly worked out is not subconsciously given preference over the others.

When a series of suggested solutions has been evaluated there will usually be more or more solutions that turn out to be better than the others. The best one, or possibly a few of the best ones, must be further detailed, which gives rise to a new series of solutions at a more detailed level. Here again one must evaluate and make a choice, but this time according to other (more detailed) criteria. After this, new details are added, and so the process continues with further solutions until all the details have been decided.

4 APPEARANCE OF THE PRODUCT

4. Appearance of the Product

IMPORTANCE OF
THE APPEARANCE

GREAT

Jewellery
Clothes
Furniture
Domestic
appliances
Radio, T.V.
tape recorders
Office
machines
Machine tools
Contractors
plant
Electrical
equipment
Engines
Valves
Nails, screws

NIL

4.1 The idea of appearance

Aesthetics

The appearance of a product is a consequence of the choice of structure, form, material, dimension and surface (including colour), in other words exactly the five basic properties that were discussed in Chapter 1.

Appearance can only be evaluated subjectively, as it can be equated with the visual impression given by the five basic properties. Appearance there-fore cannot be measured and, of course, it is this fact which gives rise to much discussion when an object looks pleasing.

When designing a product one cannot leave its appear-ance out of account, but the degree to which this influences the form depends on the type of product in question. For certain products, appearance is a basic quality. This applies for instance to jewellery, clothes and furniture. There are also products where the appearance is immaterial, e.g. carburettors, ferrules, nails and screws. All other products are somewhere in between these extremes, as suggested in the table on the left.

What exactly is good appearance, and what is characteristic for a product that we would call beautiful? Unfortunately, a satisfactory answer has never been found. The nearest one can get is that it is possible to identify certain features that together give us an idea of why some things are ugly, while others are beautiful. Aesthetics, i.e. the study of beauty, is concerned with these questions. It is not possible to draw up rules that will ensure a beautiful product, but on the other hand we can give some guidelines, which a designer can use with a certain probability of a reasonable result. The rest of this chapter deals with such guidelines.

Speculation on why certain articles can give an onlooker an aesthetic experience has always engaged humanity. Some people have found beauty in nature, others in strict geometric shapes and others again in swelling curves and garish colours. These people may all be right in their own way. The difference in taste of different people could often be the reason why some articles are felt to be beautiful, while others are not. However, if something is really beautiful most people can agree. Therefore, it must be possible to find certain characteristics that are common to the feeling which gives one an aesthetic experience.

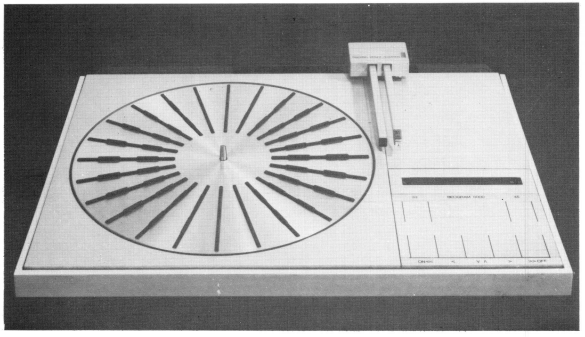

Figure 141   An aesthetic product characterised by unity and order (Courtesy Bang & Olufsen)

Beauty may in the first instance be characterised by its opposite — ugliness. When an article is felt to be ugly it may be because it is discordant, shoddy, careless, bitty, defective or badly made. Beauty is the complement of ugliness, and from this we may get an indication of what beauty is. One must, however, remember that between ugliness and beauty lies the neutral and uninteresting. So beauty must possess other qualities apart from not being ugly. The most important characteristics are unity and order, (see Figure 141).

Unity

A product ought to appear as a finished complete unit, where the separate elements and details belong together in a logical and harmonic way. There must be no elements that stand out as if they did not belong, and that arouse questions or surprise. It will also be unfortunate if the product looks as if some part is missing. It can be generally said that any disturbance of the overall impression mars the appearance.

A harmonic unit may be achieved if the component elements are related in some way, e.g. by common form (basic shapes, curves, etc.), similarity in surface structure and in the choice of colours, (see Figure 142).

Order

Two of the qualities already mentioned in connection with ugliness were carelessness and disorder. It is therefore natural to examine how far the idea of 'order' belongs to the aesthetic product. Sometimes order in itself may satisfy an aesthetic need.

The highest degree of order — strict repetition — will, however, often become too monotonous, while a freer and more varied order can make the product an exciting sensual experience. The degree of order that is most suitable depends on the complexity of the product, in the sense that the more complex the product the higher a degree of order is needed. How elements can be arranged with a certain variety is more closely examined in section 4.3. The importance of order for aesthetic experience is illustrated in Figure 143.

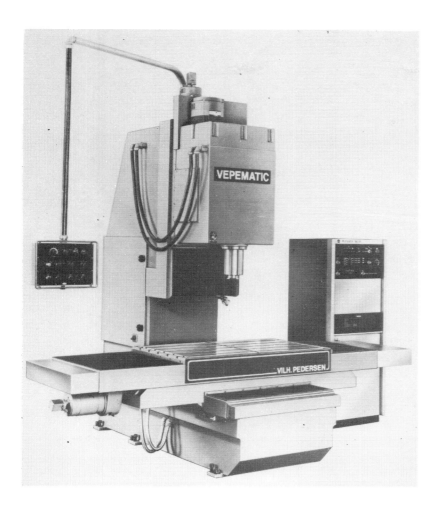

Figure 142   Unity and lack of unity. Above, a programmable machine tool that constitutes a harmonic unit (courtesy Vilh. Pedersens Machine Factory Ltd.). Below, a car where the superstructure and the chassis do not seem to belong together

Figure 143   Order and disorder. Above, an offset writing machine where the separate form elements express order in respect of both form and arrangement. (Courtesy of Helioprint Ltd). Below, a typical prototype that bears the stamp of disorder. In this case one does not worry about appearance but about function

4.2 Form elements

Most industrially manufactured products are built up of a number of elements of a relatively simple geometrical form. In the more complex products and machines the elements are put together into sub-systems, which again are often in the form of known geometrical shapes.

The product is therefore usually characterised by a number of 'form elements', which together make up the outer form. These form elements help to give the product its character, whether this fact has been taken deliberate advantage of or not.

The form elements that are met most often are the basic shapes of the cube — the cylinder, the sphere, the pyramid, the cone and the ellipsoid or parts of these, see Figure 144. The box and the cylinder are the form elements most often used, with the result that the majority of products consist of lines and planes at right angles to each other. Several reasons for this situation may be mentioned:

The Mind.   'The eye' is naturally used to perceiving vertical and horizontal as the main visual directions, and it is natural to think in terms of these directions.

Models.   When it is necessary to supplement the imagination this may be done by using a model. By far the most widely used type of model is a drawing, most often in right-angled projection. In this sort of projection much the easiest objects to sketch are those that broadly consist of planes parallel to the projection planes.

Technologies. Manufacturing processes favour objects with planes at right angles to each other and those that can be turned on a lathe.

The above comments must not be regarded as arguments for the form elements always having to be simple geometrical forms, for naturally the designer has always his freedom inside the limits of the

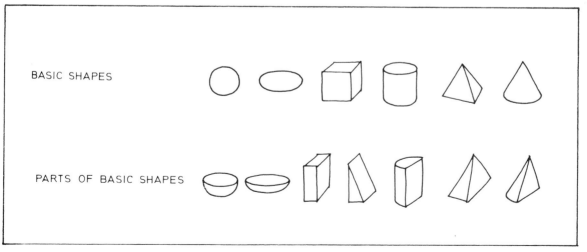

BASIC SHAPES

PARTS OF BASIC SHAPES

Figure 144   Form elements

criteria. However, if a number of products are studied on the basis of the form elements they consists of, it will be found that the basic shapes in Figure 144 have been used. Figure 145 shows this for a number of small components. In the more complex products shown in Figures 146 to 149 the basic shapes are used in the form design of the smallest elements up to the construction of the total system.

Thinking in terms of form elements is important to the designer, because the basic shapes can be used as means of getting ideas, both when working on the total form and when deciding on the form of the elements (as described in section 2.3). It is, however, not enough to merely emphasise the importance of the idea of form elements. The designer must know that the correct integration of the form elements is essential to the appearance of the product. The following section, therefore, shows what happens when several form elements are put together, and what can be done to achieve a harmonious result.

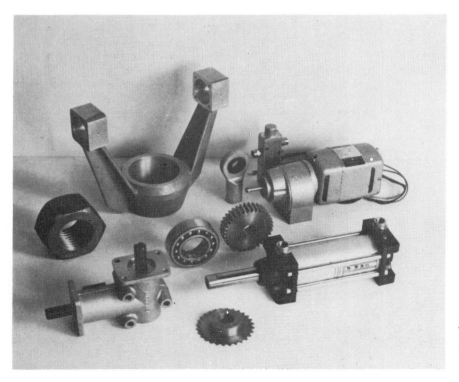

Figure 145   A number of smaller components in which the form elements from Figure 144 can be recognised

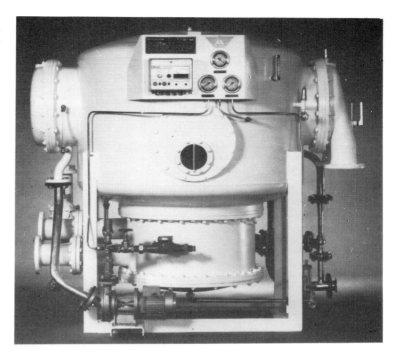

Figure 146   Fresh water plant. Note the clearly defined form elements both in the total form and in the details (Courtesy of Atlas Ltd.)

Figure 147   An automatic lathe with many form elements (Courtesy of Boehringer)

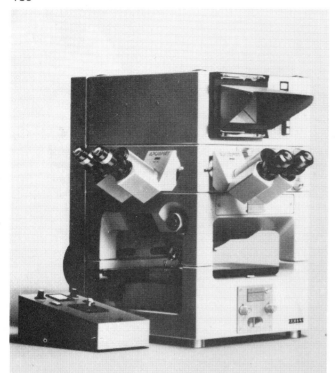

Figure 148 Microscope built up of simple geometric basic forms (Courtesy of Carl Zeiss)

Figure 149 Excavator built up of pronounced form elements (Courtesy of J. C. Bamford Exc.)

4.3 Combining form elements

Visual balance

Let us examine two isolated form units or form elements and try to combine them. If the form elements are moved towards each other we notice that, at a certain distance, they seem to belong together and have formed a group (see Figure 150 (a) and (b)). The idea of group is fundamental to our visual perception. If we study a number of elements in a group they will affect each other, apart from just seeming to belong together. We will feel that the elements are visually more or less in balance.

A visual balance may be achieved by symmetry, or it may be asymmetrical. In the latter case the component elements must be shaped and arranged in relation to each other in such a way that there seems to be the same 'weight' (a combination of form and colour) on both sides of an imaginary

central line. Visual balance is illustrated in Figure 150 (c) to (e), where (c) shows it achieved by symmetry, (d) an asymmetrical balance and (e) a visual imbalance.

If a group of form elements are not in balance they may 'offend the eye'. One must especially guard against cases where the total form is very nearly symmetrical, but not quite. A good rule of thumb is, that the form must be either symmetrical or sufficiently asymmetrical for it to be clearly deliberate and not simply lopsidedness.

Figures 151 and 152 show examples of visual balance on the front of two meters. Figure 153 shows a vacuum pump in visual imbalance (it looks as if it will topple over), and Figure 154 a visually balanced vertical drill.

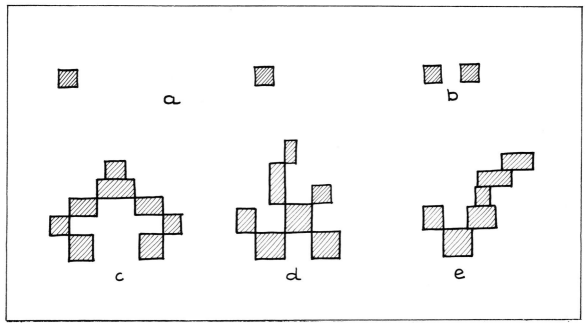

Figure 150   The group effect between two elements (a and b), visual balance (c, symmetrical; d, asymmetrical) and visual imbalance (e)

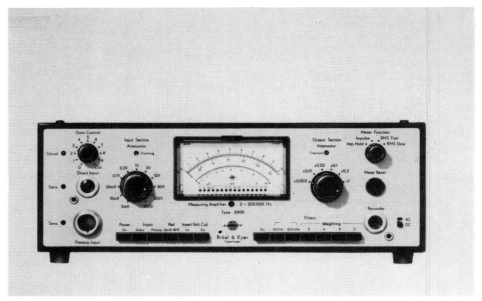

Figure 151   Visual balance through symmetry (Courtesy of Bruel & Kjaer)

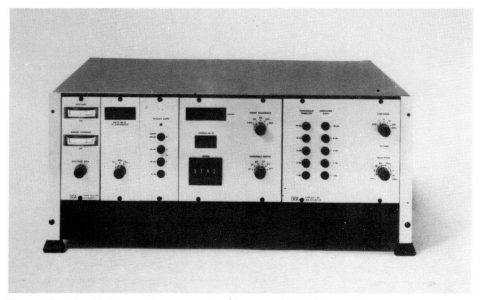

Figure 152   Visual balance without symmetry (Coutesy of DISA Electronic Ltd.)

Figure 153   Vacuum pump which gives an impression of visual imbalance

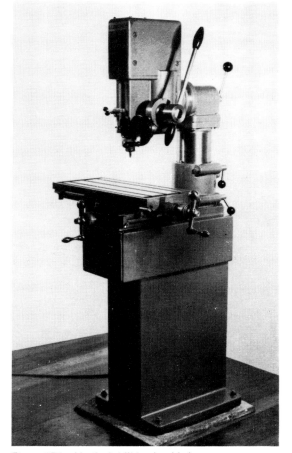

Figure 154   Vertical drill in visual balance

Rhythm

In the section of aesthetics (page 143) it was mentioned that one important characteristic of beautiful products is order. At the same time it was emphasised that the degree of necessary order depends on the degree of complexity. The idea of order is thus most pronounced when many elements are present.

Let us consider a great number of similar elements as shown in Figure 155a. The arrangement where they are equally spaced represents the highest degree of order, but put together in this way the elements constitute an uninteresting row. How can we make the group of elements more exciting? We can introduce a certain variation which we repeat with suitable intervals. This 'order with variation' or 'Rhythm' may be carried out by using the variation parameters from section 2.3. These are arrangement, dimension, number and form of elements (this includes their colour). Figure 155b shows the elements in groups where rhythm is introduced in different ways.

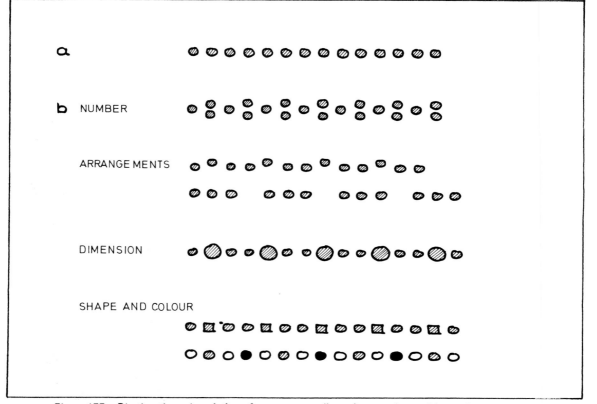

Figure 155   Rhythm through variation of arrangement, dimension, number and form of the elements

The extent to which rhythm is introduced into a group of elements depends, as already mentioned, not only on the complexity (number and dissimilarity of the elements) but also on personal taste. Figure 156 shows a design of a ship's transmitter where rhythm helps to make the appearance exciting. Rhythm has been achieved by varying the arrangement and the dimensions.

Rhythm based on varying the form of the elements can also be a powerful tool. In the cars shown in Figure 157 the shape of windows and doors is emphasised by the system of lines which they form. The arrangement, shape and angle of the lines together form a rhythm, that has a different character for the different cars.

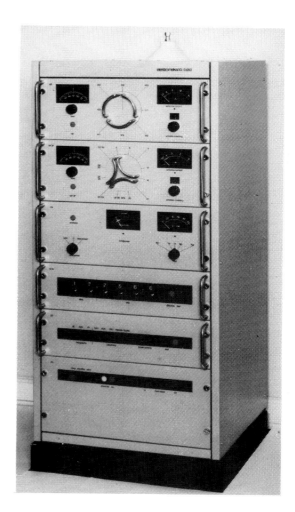

Figure 156   A ship's transmitter. The rhythm is achieved by varying the arrangement and the dimensions of the deals; alternating between rectangular and round elements and making the module heights different

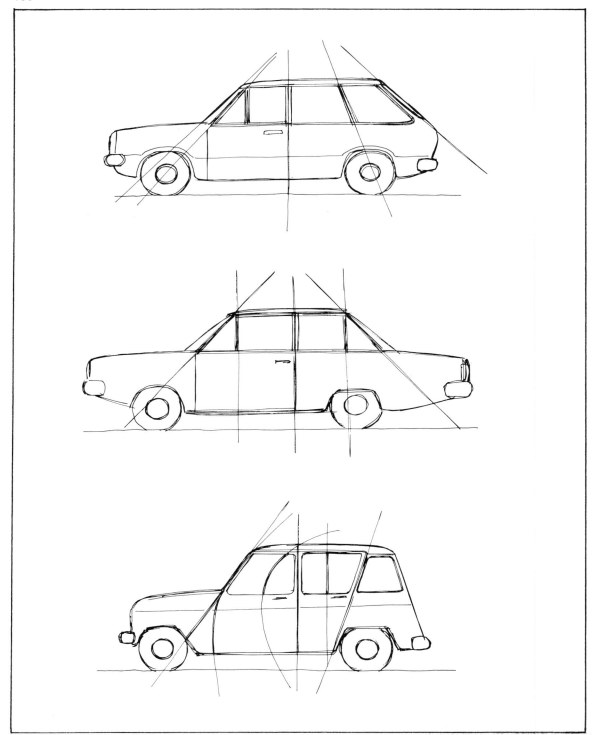

Figure 157   Three cars where the prominent lines give different rhythms

Proportions

The idea of unity, mentioned in the section on aesthetics is an important *quality.* The form elements must be suited to each other in a logical and harmonious way, and common features in their surface, structure and colour are therefore necessary. One of the parameters that can help to underline the overall impression is the proportion.

Man has always been preoccupied with the idea of a connection between proportion and beauty. There are examples of ideal measurements for beautiful human beings, and for instance, the Golden Section, which is a mathematically determined ratio between two lines A and B, defined by

$$\frac{A}{B} = \frac{B}{A-B}.$$

This gives: $\frac{A}{B} = \frac{1}{2}(1+\sqrt{5}) \simeq 1.618.$

A rectangle with this ratio between its sides is characterised by being divisible into a square and another rectangle with the same ratio between its sides, see Figure 158. Throughout the ages many people have considered this rectangle to be perfection.

Ratios such as 2:3, 3:5, 5:8, 8:13 etc are even closer approximations to the Golden Section. These proportions are applied in a great many areas. For instance, textbooks on photography teach the advisability of placing the most important part of the picture in such a way that it divides the sides in the ratio 2:3 or 3:5. These proportions may be recognised in many products.

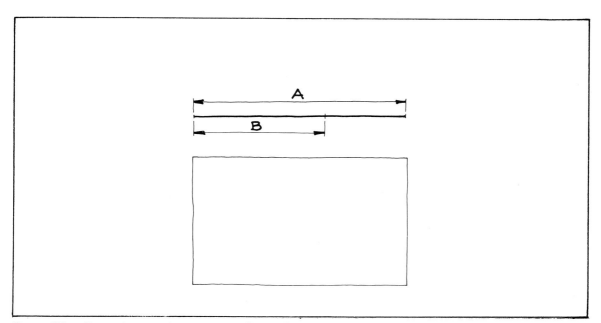

Figure 158   Above, division of a line by the Golden Section. Below, a rectangle in proportions corresponding to the Golden Section

Repeated use of certain proportions in the elements of a product may, among other things, result in the appearance of similar elements. This may also contribute greatly to the product appearing as a harmonious unit. Figure 159 shows a gramophone, where there are four similar rectangles and two squares.

A convenient aid to determining the proportions is the use of modules, the basic size or a basic area, which in various ways can be assembled into larger elements. Modules can naturally have many other advantages such as reducing costs through standard-isation, and also flexibility, but a discussion of these is outside the scope of the book. Using modules to divide an area into sections, e.g. on control panels, is a convenient way of fitting elements of different sizes as a whole.

Figure 160 shows a haemodialysis apparatus, i.e. a control unit used in conjunction with an artificial kidney for treating patients with chronic kidney complaints. Dials, control lamps, etc are grouped in sections created by dividing the outer area into 3, respectively 5, parts. The modules of height and width are in the ratio of 5:3.

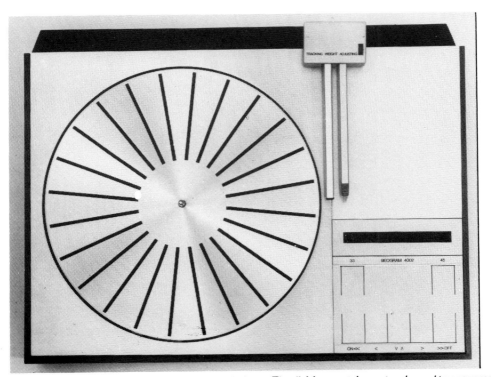

*Figure 159   Division of the surface of a record player. The division contains rectangles and two squares
(Courtesy of Bang & Olufsen)*

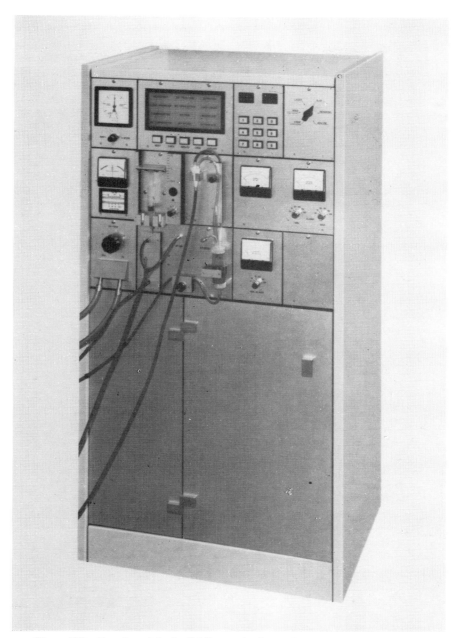

Figure 160   Use of modules in dividing up the front of a haemodialysis apparatus (Courtesy of the Institute of Product Development, The Technical University of Denmark)

Lines and planes

Occasionally, when form elements are put together unexpected visual effects will arise. The visual impression obtained when looking at a unit is not just the sum of the impressions from the elements. These influence each other visually. The visual effect is the reason why one must pay attention to the lines and planes in a product, so that a form design can be created where these are in relation to each other.

The qualities of unity and order depend on the run of the lines and planes. One therefore usually tries to give the prominent lines in the product the same character, e.g. straight lines, curves and lines at a certain angle, see Figures 161 and 162.

Continuity in the run of the individual lines is also significant. Figure 163 shows examples of the way in which a discontinuous run of lines attracts attention unfavourably.

Figure 161   Pumps and scales marked by, respectively, curved and flat planes (Courtesy of DAE Pumps Ltd and Rex Scales Factory Ltd)

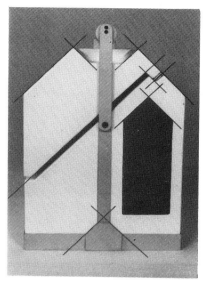

Figure 162 *A perfusator (a box for preserving and transporting living kidneys before a transplant). In the form are found a number of similarly inclined lines (Courtesy of the Lab. of Engineering Design, The Technical University of Denmark)*

Figure 163   Examples of lines which attract unfavourable attention

Joints

Joints between form elements can give rise to both constructional and visual problems. If two planes or edges meet tightly with an uncovered dividing line it will often demand unreasonable exactitude and parallelism. It is, therefore, worth noting that from a visual point of view one can adopt two attitudes to joints:

1. The elements are so designed that the joint on the whole isunnoticed, that is to say that the demand for exactitude is accepted or that the joint is hidden, e.g. by paint.

2. The joint is emphasised and deliberately used as part of the form characteristics of the product. There are several methods which can be used to achieve this — distance between the elements — grooving — staining the groove dark — covering the joint with a moulding or something similar.

Figures 164 to 167 show different examples of ways of solving the problem of joints.

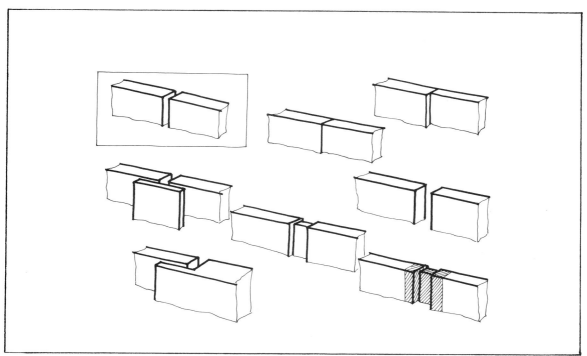

Figure 164   Different possibilities for joining two elements end-on

164

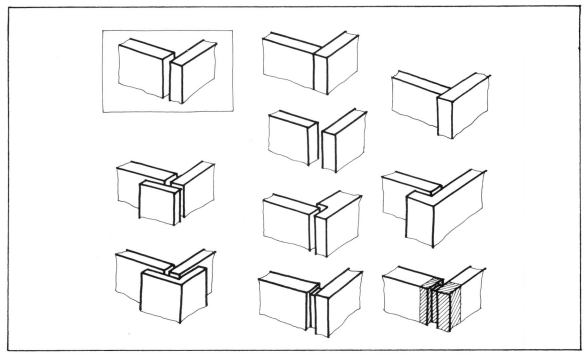

Figure 165   Different possibilities for joining two elements at right angles

Figure 166   Examples of joints. (See also Figures 164 and 165)

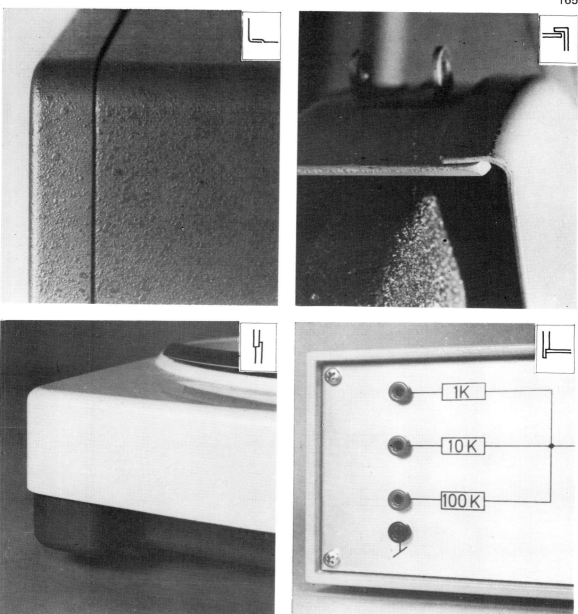

Figure 167   Examples of joints. (See also Figures 164 and 165)

4.4 Means of expression

Lightness

Based on associations when looking at the form there are certain qualities which are expected in a product. In other words, it is felt that the form can express something. This fact may be consciously used by the designer, either to emphasise certain of the product's characteristics or to mitigate possible undesirable ones.

One quality that can be stressed through the form is lightness. Figure 168 shows two situations where an object seems to have been made lighter.

In the first example, the lower part of the object has been shaped as a plinth or legs, which gives the impression that the object does not rest so heavily on the foundation. The other example is a projecting part which can be made lighter by sloping the bottom line upwards.

Figures 169 and 170 show how the diagrammatic examples in Figure 168 can be applied in designing products.

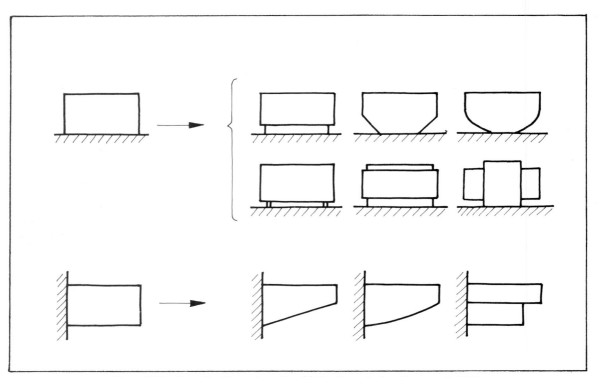

Figure 168   Two situations where the object appears to have been made lighter

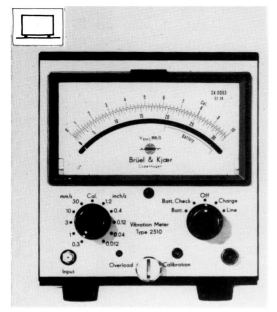

Figure 169 *Products where the form expresses lightness (see also Figure 168). The objects shown are: top left, a vibration meter. (Courtesy of Brüel and Kjaer); top right, a teamaker. (Courtesy of Lab. for Engineering Design, The Technical University of Denmark). Below, a workbench. (Courtesy of Brown and Sharpe)*

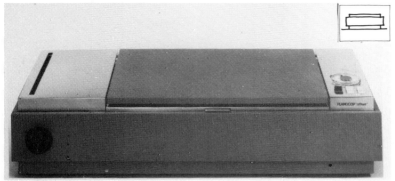

Figure 170   Further products where the form expresses lightness (see also Figure 168). The objects shown are: top left, a photocopier. (Courtesy of Eskofot Ltd);   middle and bottom left, front of car and side view of car front (Courtesy of Sunbeam and Opel); middle right, a TV set (Courtesy of Bang and Olufsen); bottom right, an operating console (Courtesy of Digital Equipment Corp.)

Weight and stability

The means that can be used to express weight and stability through the form, aim at placing the centre of gravity low down. For this purpose sloping lines or 'heavy' curves are useful. It is a fact, as far as sloping lines are concerned, that a single line expresses instability, while two lines leaning towards each other express a high degree of stability, as shown in Figure 171a. Figure 171b demonstrates how bodies with slightly concave sides are heavy compared to bodies with convex sides. Figure 171c shows examples of ways in which these two effects can be used to accentuate the stability of a box-shaped body. In some of the suggestions the form is divided into two form elements, which at the same time gives greater freedom in choosing proportions.

Products, which as a result of their function are heavy and solid, can be shaped so that this is expressed in the form. Figure 172 shows some machines that convey stability and strength.

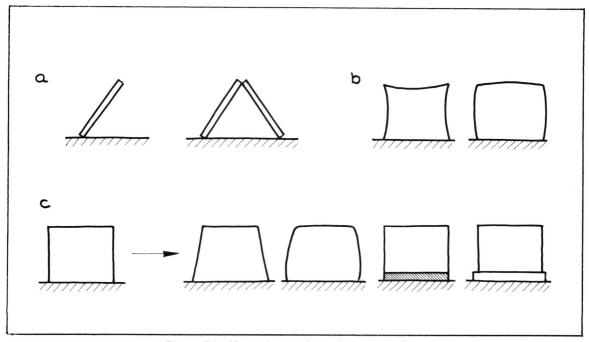

Figure 171   Means of expressing weight and stability

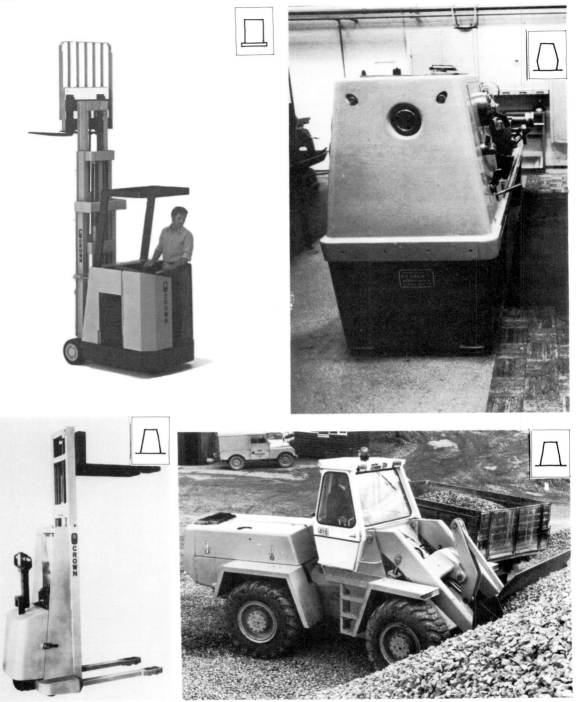

Figure 172   Products designed in a way that accentuates weight and stability, left, two fork lift trucks. (Courtesy of Crown); top right, a lathe (Courtesy of Drehbank, Colchester); bottom right, an excavator (Courtesy of J. C. Bamford Excavators Ltd)

Movement

An impression of movement and speed can, like stability, be achieved by using sloping lines, although in another way. Two lines that meet in a point give associations with an arrow, provided that the angle between them is not too great. It is therefore possible to let the form underline movement by using sloping or slightly curved lines at a relatively slight angle to the direction of movement, see Figure 173. The movement may be further emphasised by accenting lines in the direction of movement, as we know from 'speed stripes' on which are painted on some cars and railway carriages, etc.

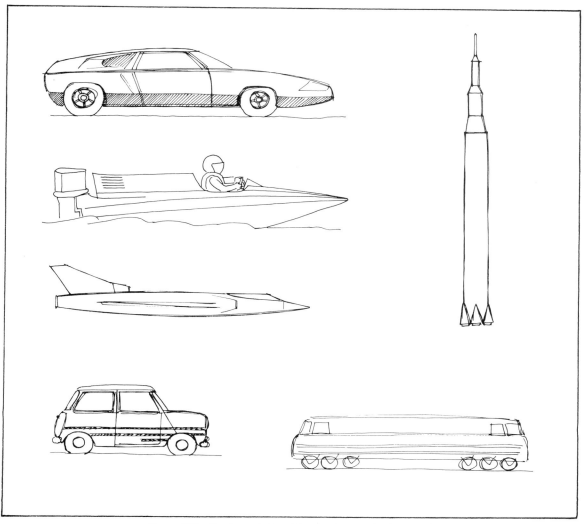

Figure 173   Products designed in way that emphasises speed

5 CASE HISTORY: CHROMOSOME APPARATUS

5. Case History: Chromosome Apparatus

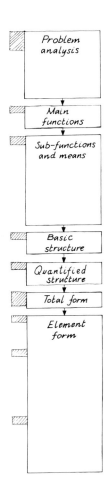

Problem
analysis

Main
functions

Sub-functions
and means

Basic
structure

Quantified
structure

Total form

Element
form

5.1 Introduction to the project

In the previous chapters we have attempted to establish a systematic approach and an organised system by which it should be possible to go through the form design stages of a project. The examples, by and large, have been taken out of the setting in which they have — or might have — belonged. For this reason it has not been possible to give a more detailed picture of the extent to which it is possible to apply the systematic methods in a design project.

It is obviously unrealistic to work systematically through all the elements in a complex project. But if one has absorbed the systematic methods there is a basis for an attitude to the work of designing which, in a given situation, results in a more or less conscious application of the system up to a certain manageable stage, while for especially difficult or critical elements one uses the thorough systematic procedure.

By more closely following the form design stages in a single design project it should be possible to observe, how in different situations one changes between systematically drawn up series of solutions and a more free and relaxed way of working with form design ideas. The project, which is described below, is the design of an apparatus for chromosome analysis. To enable this case history to be seen in the right perspective the table on the left shows which parts of the complete project are being studied.

Chromosomes carry our inherited characteristics. In each cell in the human body is a complete collection of these. They are found in the so-called genes, which normally exist in a cell nucleus separate from the rest of the cell. When the cell divides, which of course is a condition for any growth and life, the

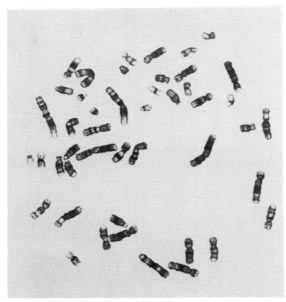

*Figure 174   Miscoscope pictures of chromosomes
in a cell*

genes gather into long threads that now fill the whole cell. These threads are what we call chromosomes. In a microscope the chromosomes may look as shown in Figure 174. When the cell division is completed the chromosomes divide lengthwise, whereby the new cell nuclei are created, that form the basis for two new cells.

Normal human beings have 46 chromosomes, but there may be abnormal chromosome combinations, which result in various diseases. In cases where somebody's chromosomes are examined a chromosome analysis is carried out, which produces a so-called karyotype diagram, where pictures of the individual chromosomes are arranged systematically, see Figure 175.

Chromosome analysis is used in various situations, including diagnosis and examination of embryonic fluid as well as research. The reason why chromosome analysis can be used in diagnosis is that there is a connection between certain diseases (e.g. mongolism) and the chromosome composition of the patients. Examination of embryonic fluid is undertaken if there is a suspicion that an embryo may have an abnormal chromosome composition.

In a slide prepared from the embryonic fluid one can observe the chromosome composition and so

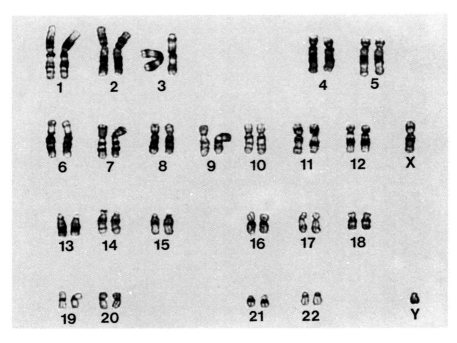

*Figure 175
Karyotype diagram*

ascertain whether this is normal or if there is something wrong. Examination of parents-to-be is made if there is a probability that a child may be born with a chromosome abnormality. From such an examination one can estimate how great this probability is. Chromosome analysis is used in research examine whether diseases with so far unknown causes may be due to chromosome abnormality. A chromosome analysis comprises the following stages: the extraction of suitable cells, preparation of the cell, staining (to make the chromosomes more distinct) and an actual analysis, in which the karyotype is made.

Only the actual analysis will be discussed here. The starting point is a prepared slide, which is put into a microscope. The slide contains several cells, and it is the first job of the laboratory assistant to find a suitable cell (i.e. one with distinct chromosomes that do not overlap). When a cell has been found a photograph is taken. For safety, one usually takes one more photograph of another suitable cell. Later, when the laboratory assistant gets the photographs back from development, the karyotype can be prepared. This is done by cutting out, arranging

and glueing onto a standard diagram all the chromosomes. After that the karyotype is ready, and an actual assessment of the chromosome composition can be made. The procedure in the manual process here described is illustrated in Figure 176.

In assessing the possibilities of making the chromosome analysis automatic, one will realise that this may be done at many levels. In many places, for instance, people are developing a system that automatically carries out all the partial processes, from seeking out a suitable cell up to the finished karyotype or similar computer material. Even if such systems may technically function they have a number of drawbacks. For one thing, they require that a computer is available, also that an operator is present, who — depending on the system — must carry out various assessments for the process to be possible.

The basis for the present project was that it was considered probable that a solution with a smaller degree of automation would be more advantageous than either the manual or the fully automatic process. So the basic idea for the project became to design an apparatus which by itself can

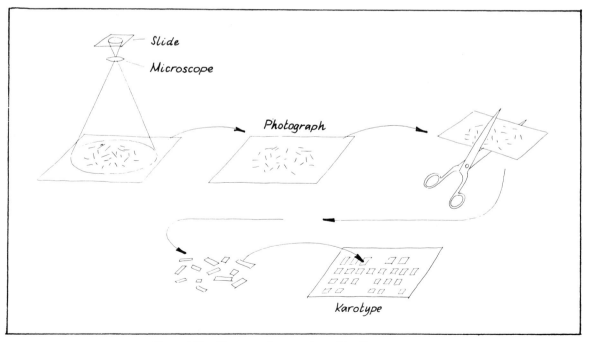

Figure 176   The manual process in making Karyotypes

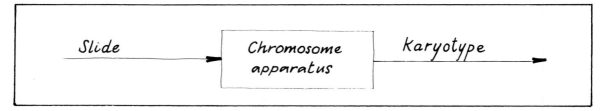

Figure 177   The chromosome apparatus as a black box

carry out the operations that the laboratory assistant had previously performed, but which makes use of his ability to identify the chromosomes. In this way it becomes possible to perform the chromosome analyses in considerably shorter time, as well as to make the apparatus cheaper, because the complicated operations — to seek out and recognise the chromosomes — are performed by the operator, while the trivial, troublesome and time consuming more mechanical operations are carried out in the apparatus. A further advantage over the manual method is the fact that the karyotype is obtained while the slide is in the microscope in the position where the cell in question is shown. This makes it possible to compare the karyotype with the cell picture in any cases of doubt. The task can now be formulated in more detail.

We want to design a system which, by using human ability to recognise patterns, makes possible an increase of the analysis capacity of a chromosome laboratory. The output from the analyses must

be a karyotype diagram printed on durable material suitable for archive storage.

How the process in Figure 177 can be split into partial processes will not be further discussed here. The division may be made in many ways, and Figure 178 shows the preferred procedure. It will be seen from the figure that it has been clearly decided which partial processes the operator and the apparatus each will perform.

The main functions that the chromosome apparatus must carry out may be seen in Figure 178. These are to create a visual picture, to delimit the particular part of the slide, to orientate it, to classify it (in the karyotype), and to expose it. It has been decided to perform the function of creating a visual picture with a traditional microscope, and the function of exposing as in an ordinary camera with a shutter. The three central main functions remain: delimitation, orientation and classification of the slide part. In the next section these three functions are taken as starting points for the search for basic structures.

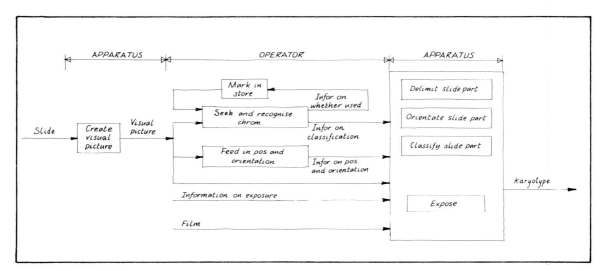

Figure 178   Chart showing the main functions which must be carried out by the chromosome apparatus

Delimit chosen
chrom. from total
microscope pict.

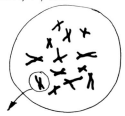

Orientate chrom.

Classify chrom.
in karyotype diagram

5.2 Basic structure

The three functions that form the basis for devising basic structures are illustrated in the table on the left. The means that can realise these are shown in Figure 179. It is assumed that optical or optical/photographic solutions are used, and not for instance electronic ones (see page 182). The methods in Figure 179 are shown at a relatively abstract level, which keeps the possibilities down to a reasonable number. The next step will now be to combine three functions into different basic structures. A great number of combinations are theoretically possible, but many of the solutions are complicated, and several have other obvious drawbacks compared to other solutions. These may be rejected straight away. In order to progress it is necessary to detail the solutions further. This is done by examining how a pencil of light can be moved, as shown in Figure 180, and also how it can be turned, what mechanical movements are necessary, etc. The many possibilities can only be assessed after various calculations and experiments, and the criteria which comes into the picture at this stage are, picture quality, space requirements, mechanical complexities, special cost circumstances, time taken, etc. The final choice is only made after a number of basic structures have been drawn up.

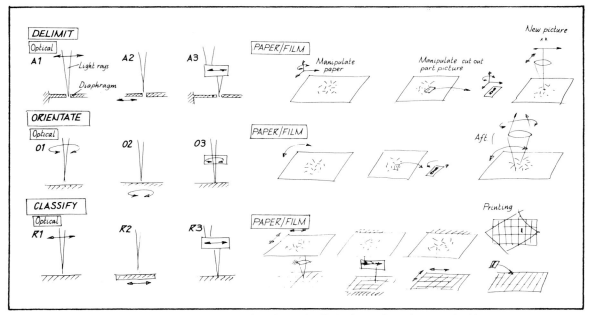

Figure 179   Means of realising the functions of delimitation, orientation and classification

From our knowledge of the partial solutions in Figure 180 the number of basic structures may be reduced to fourteen realistic suggested solutions as shown in Figure 181. In the purely optical solutions we have not distinguished between the different part solutions with mirrors, lenses and prisms in Figure 180, but solutions that include optical fibres are shown separately, as they are essentially different from the others.

The basic structure which was found to be most suitable is shown in detail in Figure 182. The starting point is the solution number 2 in Figure 181, and the following part solutions from Figure 180 —

delimitation with the aid of a sliding lens, and classification by means of a tilting mirror. Orientation is performed by Abbe's prism.

One important part of the basic structure has not yet been mentioned, namely the part which involves the operator. Among a number of possibilities it has been decided that the operator will have a picture of the slide on a screen in front of him. The input to the apparatus will take place in such a way that information on delimitation and orientation is given through a mechanical viewfinder, which the operator points at the desired chromosome, while information on the classification is passed through a keyboard.

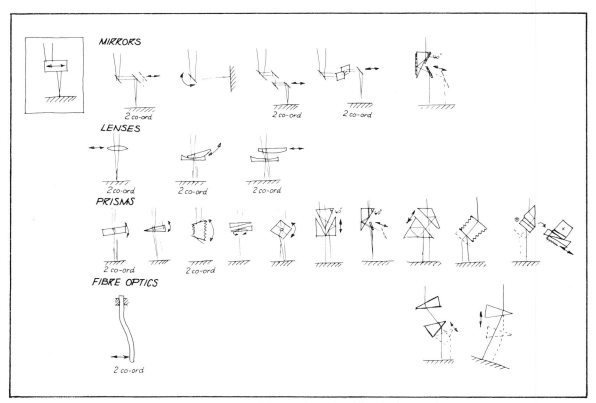

Figure 180   Means of realising the function of 'moving' a ray of light

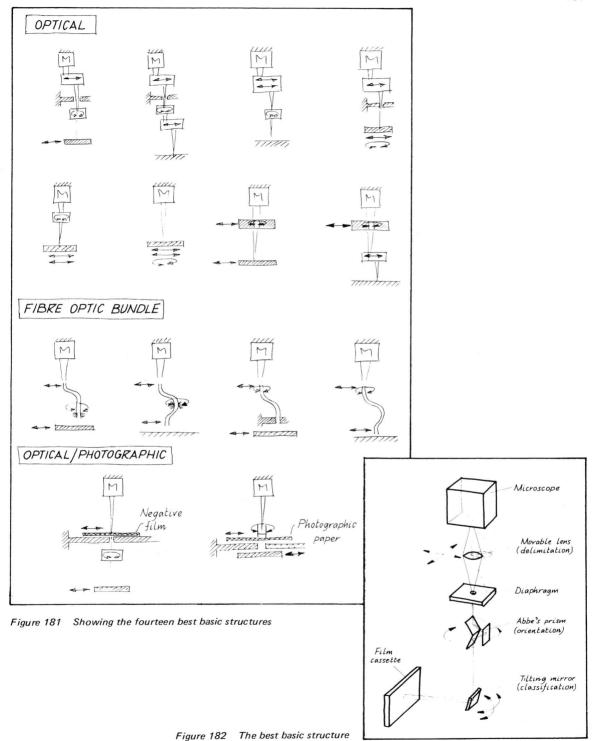

Figure 181   Showing the fourteen best basic structures

Figure 182   The best basic structure

5.3 Quantified structure

On the basis of the chosen basic structure in Figure 182 a number of crucial specifications and the main data must be laid down, so that a karyotype of the desired quality can be produced. The most important data of the constituent sub-systems are examined and decided on (type of microscope, film cassette, length of light rays, etc) and after that, modelling of various quantified structures can take place, as described in Chapter 2. In the first instance a number of sketches are made, as shown in Figure 183. These, however, can only give a certain general impression of the possibilities, while a more detailed assessment of the quantified structure requires a three-dimensional structure model. This is made of plastic foam in such a way that all the elements can be easily moved about. Figure 184 shows a number of the best quantified structures.

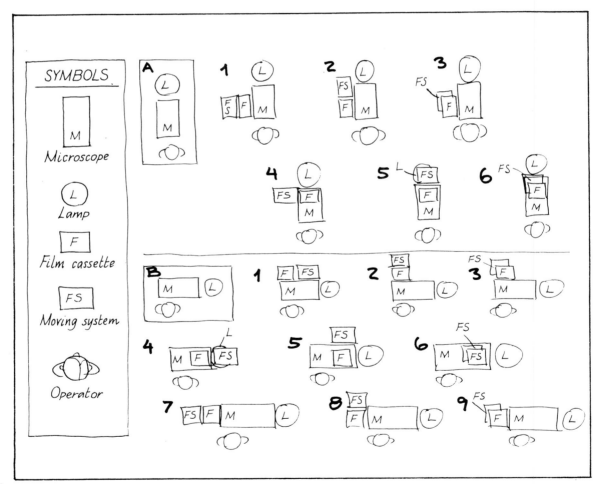

Figure 183   Quantified structures on the basis of the best basic structure shown in Figure 182

The three-dimensional structure models make it possible to evaluate such aspects as working space for the operator, mechanical complexity, heat (film not too close to the lamp), height, width and depth of the instrument etc. On the basis of such an evaluation the quantified structure marked B—9 in Figures 183 and 185 is chosen.

The chosen structure is shown in greater detail in Figure 184. The operator has in front of him a screen on which is projected a picture of the cell with the chromosomes. Information on the position and orientation of the chosen chromosome is transferred mechanically to the movable lens (three different projecting lenses) and to the Abbe's prism. In this way the picture of the desired chromosome is focussed and orientated. The tilting mirror, which performs the classification of the chromosome picture, is positioned through a moving system that is activated by a keyboard with a control knob for each chromosome.

Apart from the karyotype, the chromosome apparatus must also be able to photograph the whole cell. This total picture can be taken when the diaphragm is removed and the tilting mirror is put in the mid position.

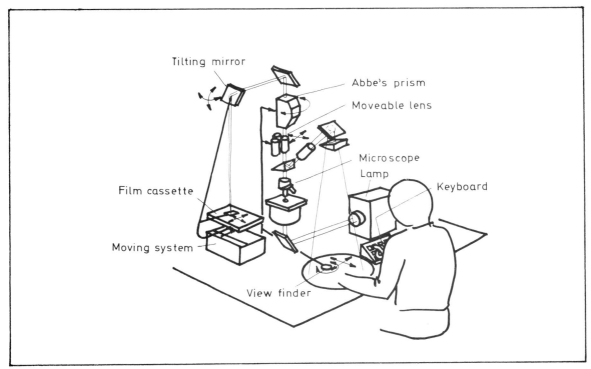

Figure 184   The chosen quantified structure

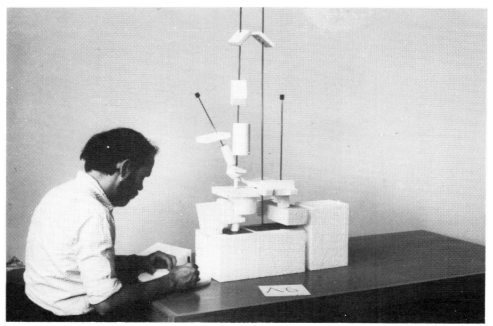

Figure 185 Quantified three-dimensional structures modelled in plastic foam. Some of the elements are fixed on spikes, so that they can be easily moved around

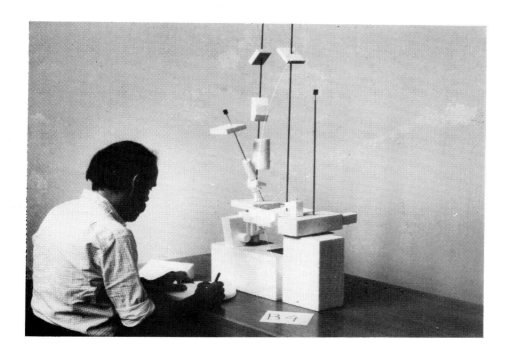

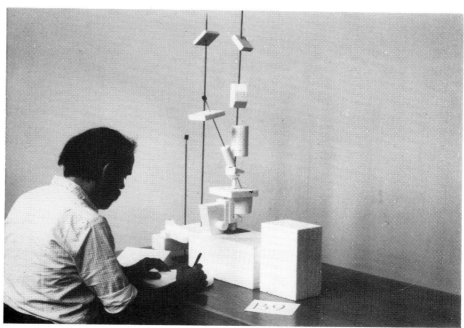

Figure 185 (continued)

5.4 Form of the total system

During the work of form designing the chromosome apparatus there is interaction between the work on the outer form and the form of the elements, as is generally expressed in the product synthesis. The description on the following pages of the way in which the form of the total system is decided on, must therefore be seen as parallel to the next section on the form of the elements.

The quantified structure in Figure 185 is taken as the starting point. As the film cassette must not be exposed to false light, a number of the constituent elements must be enclosed in a lightproof screening. The very first rough design proposals are arrived at by varying the form geometry and the form division, as shown in Figures 186 and 187. The pages following Figure 194 describe how the design is gradually chosen.

The ideas are modelled in various ways as the work progresses. Depending on the situation rough sketches, scale drawings, and three-dimensional models in plastic foam, wood and cardboard are used. These models have been very important in connection with the choice of form concept, see Figures 190 and 194.

The criteria that count when choosing between alternative designs, stem first of all from the user and from the production. As far as the user is concerned, it is a question of working posture, accessibility, cleaning, adjustment and maintenance, psychological factors (how is the apparatus experienced?) and appearance (unity, order, visual balance). From the production come criteria in connection with the manufacturing process, choice of material, production quantities and assembly.

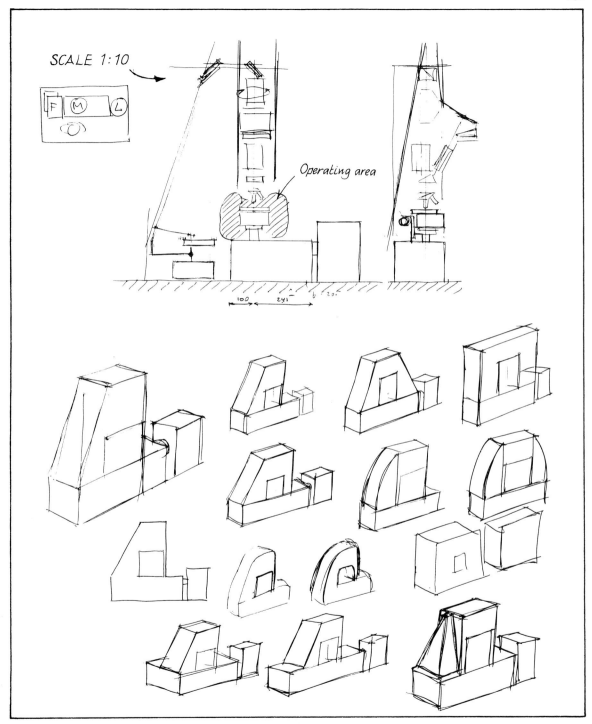

SCALE 1:10

Operating area

Figure 186   The starting point for form designs is obtained by drawing contour lines closely around the elements to be screened. Varying the form geometry gives the first rough form design suggestions

FORM DIVISION

Figure 187   Variation of form division. These sketches form the starting point for a number of the suggestions on the following pages

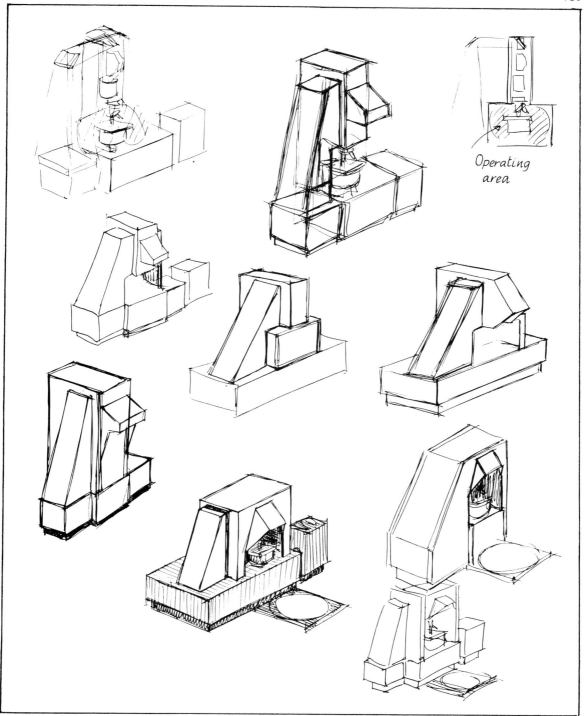

Operating area

Figure 188　The first series of form concepts

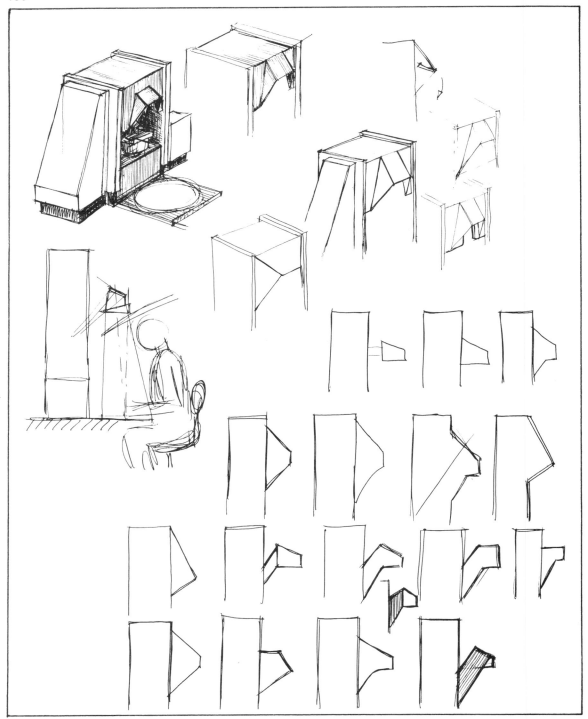

Figure 189 A general problem is examined, namely the form design of the screen around the operator's mirror. Form geometry and form division are used as variation parameters

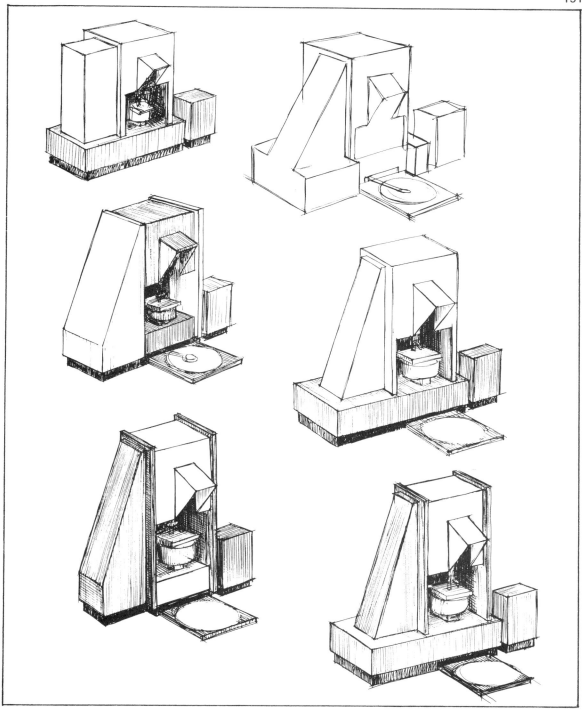

Figure 190 A number of detailed form concepts which appear fairly realistic. A three-dimensional model of the suggestion bottom right showed, however, the unfortunate psychological effect that the apparatus is felt to be oppressive, almost like a wall in front of the operator

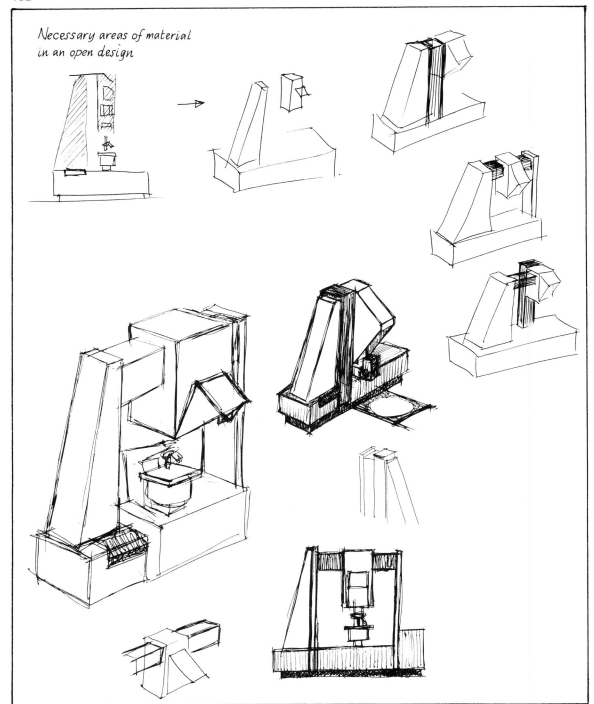

Necessary areas of material
in an open design

Figure 191 On the basis of the experience gained from the previous suggestions we can examine the possibilities of more open form designs. At the top can be seen the areas the elements occupy, and three possible areas of material are shown

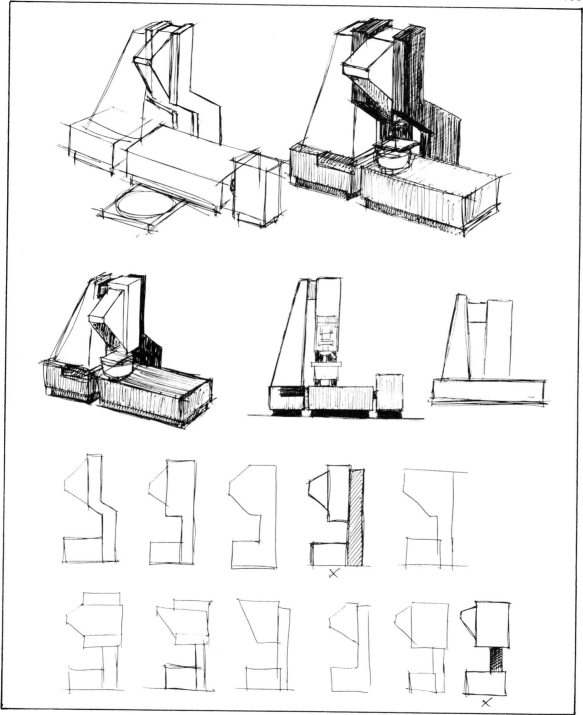

Figure 192 Examination of the problems surrounding a partly open framework. Variation of the form division is shown below

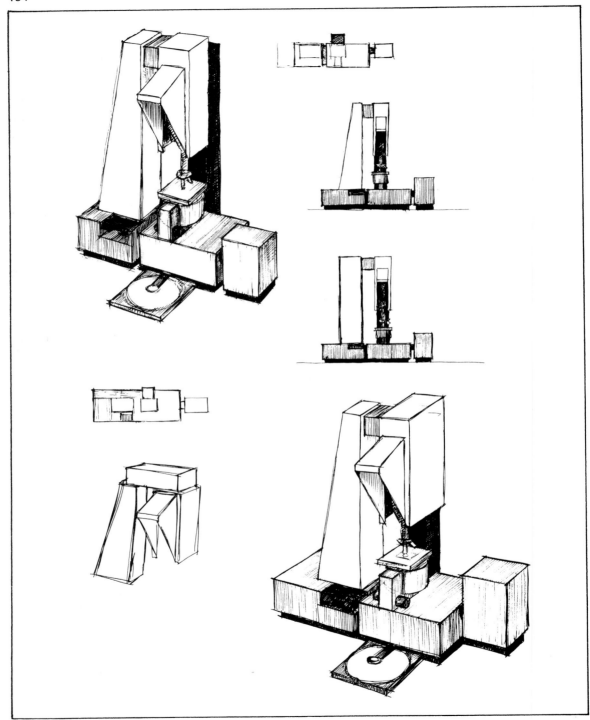

Figure 193 Two realistic design suggestions

Figure 194   Form models corresponding to the two suggestions in Figure 193. Before the final choice can be made one form model must be painted. This makes it possible to assess whether the problems of the visual balance indicated in Figure 192 can be overcome by an appropriate choice of colour

5.5 Form of the elements

The design of the elements constitutes a very complex series of activities, partly because there are many elements of widely different character, partly because their details are designed simultaneously with the choice of materials, dimensions and surfaces, and finally, as already mentioned, because the external form is closely connected with the form of the elements. First, it must be emphasised that there is an intermediate stage involving decisions on sub-systems, such as a transfer mechanism from view finder to projecting lens, and a control system that transfers information from the keyboard to the tilting mirror. These sub-systems are treated in exactly the same way as the total system, that is to say that one goes through the stages of basic structure, quantified structure, etc. corresponding to a new product synthesis on a smaller scale. An example is shown in Figure 195, which deals with transmission mechanisms to the tilting mirror. Figure 196 shows how structure variation can be applied to such a sub-system.

The form design of the frame is illustrated in Figures 197 and 198. These show how thinking in terms of functional surfaces gives a clear starting point for a number of suggestions, where the arrangement of the areas of material is varied. The frame is an example of the way in which the form of an element is connected with the external form of the apparatus, as part of the frame is visible and even constitutes an essential part of the external form.

The further one advances in detailing the elements of the chromosome apparatus, the more the character of the form design work is altered towards deciding on a number of details in connection with the functional surfaces. It is first of all a question of deciding on the points where the elements are to be joined together, as shown, for instance, in Figure 199, which deals with the base box and the covering screens. One of the external functional areas of great importance is the viewfinder shown in Figure 200.

The criteria for the design of the elements are mostly concerned with two things. First the function, i.e. precision, reliability, stability, strength and rigidity, and secondly the production, manufacturing process, production quantities, assembly, and as a consequence of these an essential criterion — production costs.

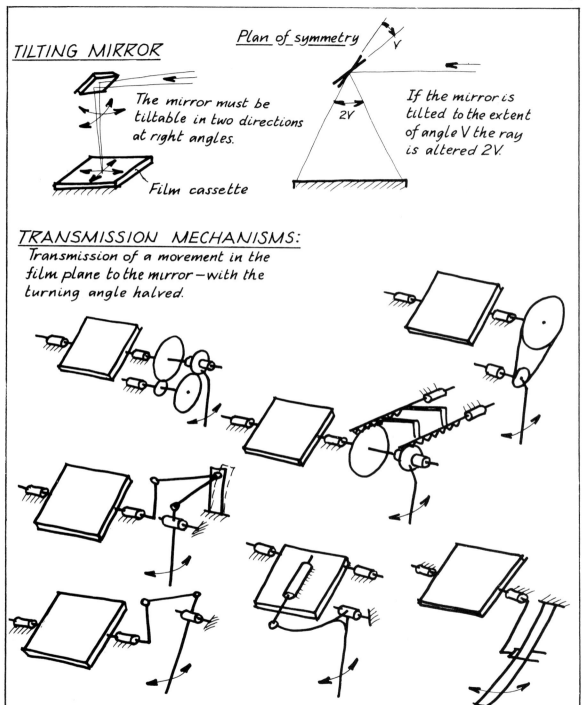

TILTING MIRROR

Plan of symmetry

The mirror must be tiltable in two directions at right angles.

Film cassette

If the mirror is tilted to the extent of angle V the ray is altered 2V.

TRANSMISSION MECHANISMS:

Transmission of a movement in the film plane to the mirror — with the turning angle halved.

Figure 195   Basic structures for transmission systems for a tilting mirror

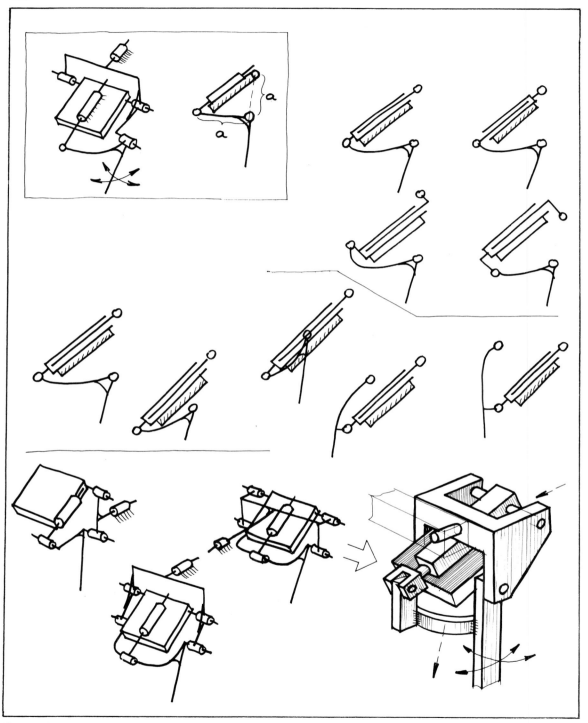

Figure 196   Variation of quantified structure for a tilting mirror. The chosen structure is shown at the bottom right on the final version

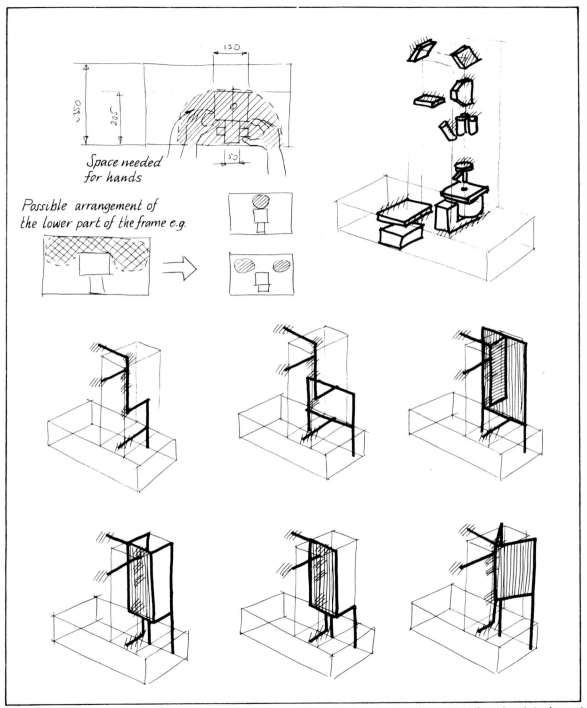

Figure 197   The first stages in the form design of the frame. Top, the functional surfaces are indicated and the banned
areas made clear. Bottom, arrangement of the areas of material are examined

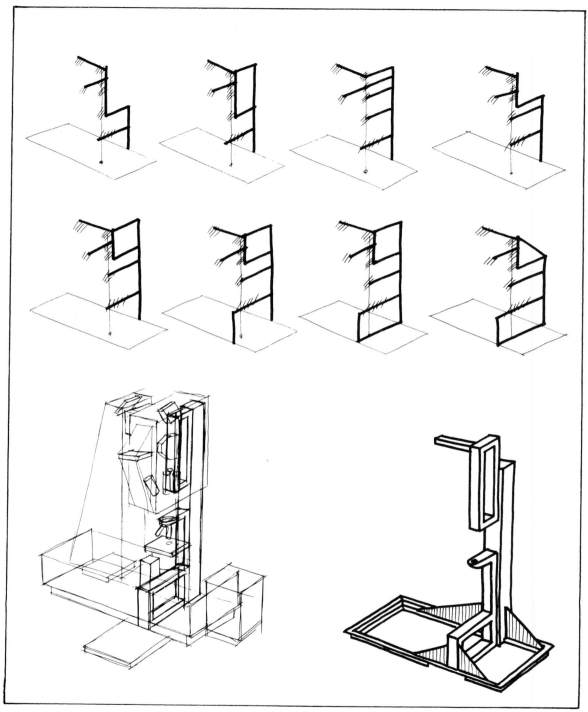

Figure 198   The form design of the frame and the total form design are closely connected. In accordance with Figure 193 a total form design is chosen where part of the frame in the shape of a column is visible. Various areas of material with a column are shown above. Below, the chosen frame

201

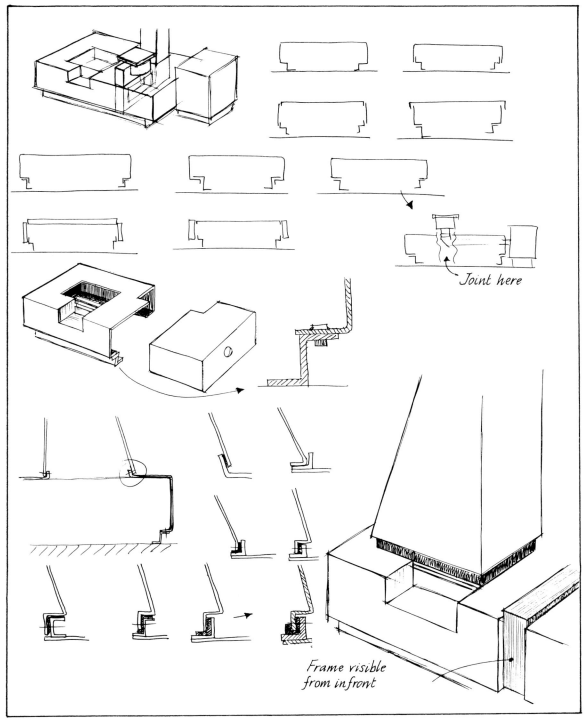

Figure 199 A base box and covering screens. Examination of possibilities of lightproof joints through varying the functional surfaces

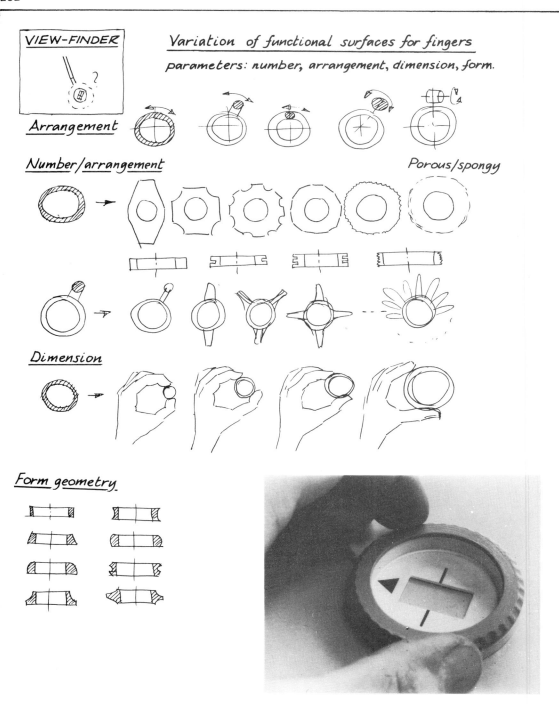

Figure 200 Variation of functional surfaces for the viewfinder. The design chosen is shown in the photograph

Figure 201   The completed chromosome apparatus (Courtesy of Lab. of Engineering Design, The Technical University of Denmark)

The design of all the elements in the chromosome apparatus is decided after drawing up sketches and plans, and the elements are finally specified in a set of working and assembly drawings which form the basis for the production. When the apparatus is assembled the time has come for testing, and for a realistic evaluation of whether it actually possesses the expected qualities. Small corrections and improvements are added, and the completed chromosome apparatus appears finally as shown in Figure 201.

It must once more be emphasised that not all the stages in the project have been described in this case history, (see the diagram in the margin on page 183). A number of experiments concerning physical feasibility, the electrical control system, various calculations, as well as working drawings have been omitted.

The case history as outlined above has an essential aim which is to form a contrast to the systematically drawn up but unconnected examples throughout the book, especially in Chapter 2. Through a case history it is possible to show the connection between the search for ideas and evaluation, and to show how situations arise in which the form methods can be applied. Finally a difference in the technique of modelling may be observed (especially drawing technique). The examples out of context must illustrate a method as clearly as possible, while in the actual application of the methods it is important to be able to hunt down solutions as quickly as possible.

From the study of the creation of the chromosome apparatus it is evident that in the final instance the systematic methods described in Chapter 2 may be applied in two ways. One is exactly as described i.e. for a systematic survey of the possible solutions. The other — and perhaps most important — way is to acquire the attitude behind the methods, so that one automatically thinks in terms of the ideas and variation patterns described, and only uses the methods consciously in particularly difficult or critical situations.

Index